THE BRIDPOR

POETRY, SHORT STORIES A

JUDGES
Roger McGough • Poetry
Jane Rogers • Short Stories
David Gaffney • Flash Fiction

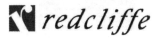

redcliffe

First published in 2015 by Redcliffe Press Ltd
81g Pembroke Road, Bristol BS8 3EA

e: info@redcliffepress.co.uk
www.redcliffepress.co.uk
Follow us on Twitter @RedcliffePress

Follow The Bridport Prize:
Follow us on Twitter @BridportPrize
www.bridportprize.org.uk
www.facebook.com/bridportprize

ISBN 978-1-908326-83-6

British Library Cataloguing-in-Publication Data
A catalogue record for this book is available from the British Library

Typeset in 10.5pt Times

Typeset by Addison Print Ltd, Northampton
Printed by Hobbs the Printers Ltd, Totton

MIX
Paper from responsible sources
FSC® C020438

Contents

ROGER McGOUGH

Poetry Report

This year the standard of entries was so high that not one of the poems I submitted anonymously reached the top 50.

I jest (about my submitting poems, not the high standard). Although it must be said that Candy Neubert and her team of readers, to whom I'm grateful for sifting through the initial 7002 entries, thought that the standard this year was disappointingly low. And if I may quote from Candy's report 'I was once told that a really fine poem "feels like a cat climbing up your leg". Sometimes there are a goodly handful of these in the final 200 but this year they feel more comfortably curled on a lap.'

However, I was more than happy to receive my box of kittens and found the judging process immensely pleasurable, and felt privileged to witness the joys and tragedies unfolding before me. I smiled, I cried, I occasionally yawned. Yes, yawned, for as many a judge will confess, giving careful reading to poem after poem can be wearisome. Not that any poems in themselves induce fatigue, but rather, the sheer volume (reflecting the success of the competition) can result in feelings of déjà-vu, and emotional overload.

One must also guard against subject and title prejudice. I remember being with a small group of judges (a dictum? a doom?) sifting through our final selections and one dismissing a poem I favoured with the words 'Cricket! I can't stand cricket. I don't care how good the poem is, it's about bloody cricket.'

I did wonder too if the time of the year and the weather can affect one's judgement? For instance, would a poem filled with summer sunshine set on a Greek island have greater appeal when read on a cold night in February? I've no idea. However, I do know that I received my bundle of poems at the end of July and that I took a hundred or so on holiday with me to Majorca in August. They were in need of a holiday. We became a familiar sight in the bars and cafes of Deia, the poems and I, inseparable, and the 25 amigos I brought home bore the smudged fingerprints of sun tan oil and vino tinto.

When Kate Wilson had asked me last year to outline to prospective competition entrants what I would be looking for, I said that I hoped to see poems that I wish I had written, and I wonder now if that was not the best advice to give. For I suspect that some poets submitted poems 'in the style of' (me) which I would never have written, nor wanted to. In other words, forget who is judging, just submit your best poem as if passing it on to a sympathetic reader.

Liz Lochhead in her Poetry Report last year noted that 'Very, very few poems were in anything other than free verse,' and that 'Most poems were about image rather than sound.' And the trend continues, rhyme being such a rarity I found myself gasping for a villanelle or the whiff of a sestina. And sad to say, the few that did appear offered more in style than content.

Content? Cancer and old age unsurprisingly, engaged the minds and hearts of many poets, and stepping inside such poems often seemed like an intrusion into a very private grief. But if grief there was, where was the rage? Politics did not engage our poets. No voices crying out against poverty and injustice, migration and global warming. Our politicians can sleep soundly in their beds, the poets are not assembling in the street outside.

Many of the poems, and this is not a criticism for I think many of my mine fall into this category, are like short films. Small surreal dramas, often funny sometimes scary, which makes me to wonder if they might have been contenders for the Flash Fiction prize. (Short story or poem? Discuss.)

The First Prize goes to 'An Elegy for Lace' which is very much a poem and a carefully crafted one. Inside the honeyed stone of the cloister walls the nuns are making lace that will adorn the necks of comtesses, perhaps a queen.

'*Bone and ivory bobbins click like needles,*
The clink of ship's masts at their mooring, as we link
Meshed nets of grenadine......' Meanwhile, in Paris, the tumbrils are being filled, the guillotine erected.

'I grow afraid, Sisters, I grow afraid.'

My Second Prize-winner, the intriguingly entitled 'The division of labour in pin manufacturing' offers advice to the emasculated job-seeker:

Nobody writes a killer pitch on a Happy Baguette napkin.
Pretending to work only makes you good at pretending.

'Camouflaged as a dead person' he wastes his days in a local cafe.

He must return to work before life loses interest in him
It's now a race against cappuccino, pastries and insignificance.

The Third Prize goes to 'How can I tell if the bluebells in my garden are Spanish?' which I imagine is the spirited, witty response to a question on Radio 4's Gardener's Question time. It may be a one-trick pony but from the opening:

They will be more flamboyant-their skirts flouncier,

...to the close:

Complete strangers-bluebells you hardly know
Will say hola to you.

...it doesn't put a hoof wrong .

Perhaps on another day, or at another time of the year, I might have awarded the first three prizes from others on my list of the ten highly commended.

'Eel', 'The Kung Fu Master's Résumé', 'British Bulldog', or 'Michelangelo's David' might have edged in. Congratulations to you all.

JANE ROGERS

Short Story Report

The first thing a short story needs to do is to make me – the reader – turn the pages. My curiosity needs to be aroused, maintained and satisfied. It is only at a second reading that I really become aware of the craft in the writing; the *ways* in which the writer is engaging me – the language, the structure, the voice, the characterisation – the techniques which are in play. And then (assuming of course it is a good story) my understanding, enjoyment and admiration deepen.

On a second reading, there were seven Bridport entries which really stood out for me, and to be honest, any one of them would have been a worthy winner of this prestigious competition. All are very fine stories. Selecting first, second and third was very difficult indeed.

In general the standard was high and I really do congratulate all entrants. It's hard writing and polishing a story and sending it off with all your hopes into the blue. I know, because I have done it myself many times, and often it has been like chucking a pebble into the sea. My stock response then is to blame the judges for poor taste, and I quite understand if you want to do that. Nevertheless, I will offer my thoughts on what made some stories weaker than others. A number of stories described a character who is lonely, bored and unfulfilled, and whose life feels rather pointless. I admit to feeling like this myself on a regular basis, but it isn't interesting and there's no suspense. A number of stories presented the viewpoint of an unfairly treated or misunderstood child. Again, this is true-to-life, but it has to be exceptionally well-handled to make it interesting. (See the winning story for this exception.) A number of stories featured violent, cruel and abusive men – but a good story needs to do more than shock and horrify; it needs to move toward some sort of resolution or catharsis, it needs a *shape*.

And my final complaint concerns tenses. The present tense is popular, but it does not work if the writer lets past and even pluperfect come crashing into it at random. Choose a tense and stick to it, please (except when the story shifts in time, obviously).

And now to the winners … 'Ping at the Zoo' is deceptively simple; an adopted Chinese girl feels isolated in America. But we are in the hands of a very skilful writer. The narrative voice is third person, restricted point of view, shifting between Ping and her mother Meifen. Ping's sections are written in such simple clear language that we can believe it is the mind of a child; and the child's observations are so precise that we can identify things for which she has no name – like the food she is served in the morning, 'tiny, hard, sweet dumplings floating in milk from a cow, which quickly go soggy.' Ping thinks a lot about food, and the reader understands this to represent many sorts of loss. It is a fine illustration of Flannery O'Connor's command that a short story should operate by showing not by saying, and by showing the concrete. The child's story is heartbreaking but there's not a scrap of sentimentality in the writing. Cutting back and forth in time, the tragic history of Ping's family is revealed with impressive economy. We are already sympathetic to the poor mother who is forced by the birth of a son to give away her daughter, before that moment comes. When it does, and Ping is taken into a house, a single sentence relates, 'Meifen watched the closed door until it disappeared in the dark, the whimpering baby hanging from her hollow chest.' A lesser writer would have told us how Meifen felt, or that she cried. Here one word, 'hollow', does it all. In short story, especially when dealing with emotion, less is always more. As Raymond Carver says, 'Get in, get out. Don't linger.' Amongst many other pleasures, I loved the way images of trees and references to their beauty and their strength are woven through the fabric of the story.

'Mannington May be Mad' is written in a very different way. It is third person again, but from the point of view of a highly educated, language-loving adult who revels in alliteration, assonance, internal rhyme, complex sentence structures – every literary trick in the book. But the story does not feel tricksy. Instead it succeeds in making the reader see and hear language afresh, making connections and revealing meanings which are more commonly furred over into cliché by thoughtless daily use. And there is a sly humour which is as built into the choice of language as it is into the hall-of-mirrors subject matter of the story itself. Very slowly, very gradually, do we come to realise the similarities between our hero and his enemy, as tiny revelations are drip-fed through his perfectly-paced account.

In third place is 'LOL' which did indeed make me laugh out loud, and was my favourite story for quite a while. It could be described as science fiction, but it reads more as a satire upon the present, than as future fiction. Dystopian visions are generally gloomy, but here the potentially terrifying subject matter is handled with a delightfully light touch. I loved the use of text salutations, and the references to blinking. If I say anymore I will give the game away, and you need to read it yourself to understand and be amused by its cleverness.

The Highly Commended stories speak eloquently for themselves, but I would like to draw attention to the wonderful variety of their subject matter (from the polar bear hunter to the teenager trapped in her high-rise Bangkok bedroom). There is also impressive variety in the types of short story here, from the futuristic, experimental style of 'The Bad Sex Awards' to the highly conventional but blackly funny crime story 'Pig Swill.'

Congratulations to all the winners. The imagination, skill and craft in your writing makes your work a joy to read. I'm pretty sure most of you are already published writers; if not, you will be soon.

And congratulations to all the entrants. After days of reading your stories my head is crammed with new ideas, images and voices. I have been privileged to enter a fantastic range of imagined worlds. There are many many stories here which contain elements of a good story, and we all know that it is incredibly hard to get *all* the elements right, so you are at least part of the way there. Keep writing, and may you go from strength to strength.

DAVID GAFFNEY

Flash Fiction Report

Reading flash fiction is like listening to chamber music. It feels close up. You can hear and see all of the different moving parts, shift focus from one phrase to the other easily, see the relationship between the instruments and the different elements of the composition. *Listen*: that's the squeak of the musician's sweat as his fingers slide along the neck of the cello; that's the tap of a shirt-cuff button on the body of a violin. When reading flash fiction the efforts of the writers are exposed in the same way; the pipes and wires are on the outside. Sometimes this is good, and sometimes not so good. Working in the close-up form you have to get everything right, every sleight of hand will be noticed, every over-emphasised pause, every unwarranted furbelow, every unearned tug on our emotions. And in a competition, we assume this is the final draft and that by this stage, any walls or pillars that are not load bearing should have been taken down. In the batch sent to me by the Bridport Prize this year I am pleased to say that many entries stood up to this close examination and it was tough to choose just six from the thousands sent in.

'Crushing Big' is a lovely story in which the crush of a schoolchild is mirrored in the parents who flirt and tease each other with promises of intimacies that never happen. I like the line 'I can see down her clean throat, glimpse her beating heart'. But it is more than just a description of a nascent love affair. It takes a turn, and a rather sinister one; the man steals the woman's coat and stows it under his mattress as a kind of fetish trophy so that he can feel her shape beneath him as he sleeps. He thinks about what is in the pockets - the bus tickets, the fluff. The strong last line hints at things to come in a tantalising way. 'The Witness' is entirely different. It's an intriguing and disturbing examination of a war atrocity which we learn partway through takes place in the concentration camp Belzec. Horrifying details are unfolded casually, in an almost offhand way, from the point of view of a worker who has been tasked with writing a hygiene report on procedures at the death camp. It's a big subject for flash fiction and demonstrates that the form is able to bear the weight of solemn, historical themes such as this. I like the line 'memory, a stone in its depth now'. 'Sense of Smell' could have ended up as an over-tricksy point-of-view reveal story, but here the reader learns who is talking early on. It is being told to us by a baby still in the womb, and is a study of the effects of the sounds and tastes and smells on the developing embryo – brilliantly described, especially that of distantly perceived tobacco from a group of schoolboys the mother walks past. It's a simple story as such and doesn't drive ahead much plot wise – but it's compelling and the story's movement is all about our growing realisation of the strange and unique point of view. And it's got one of the best last lines I've read – 'Let's begin.' 'The Price of Truth' caught my eye because it's a blackly humorous piece about the way us writers can often appear to be cold distant creatures who harvest stories from the souls of those around us with an eye only on novelty, entertainment, and self-aggrandisement. It does this with a neat little plot with a banging punch line. Next – well, we've all been left in a car outside a pub with nothing but a packet of crisps for entertainment – it still happens to me now, in fact. 'Good at Crisps' is a great description of this childhood memory, with some nice accounts of the many different ways you can ingest fried potato snacks. In 'Encounter', a hitchhiker gets a lift from God and is transfixed by the different ways God chooses to present himself to the world, all in the space of a few minutes.

All in all it was a pleasure to read such a varied bunch of short-short stories, and congratulations to the winners.

POETRY FIRST PRIZE

KATHY MILES

An Elegy for Lace

In memory of the lacemakers of Chantilly, and the Sisters of Compiègne (also lacemakers), executed in the French Revolution

In late afternoon, a tapestry of apples,
shadows stippled on the orchard's hem.

Scents of garlic and wild violet, the linnet
keening on the wind, a slur of sun in the grass.

A dragonfly, his wings stretched webs of thread,
rises in the bleach of evening dusk.

Our hands a quiet prayer of lace, inside
the honeyed stone of the cloister walls.

We loop the silky tussels of yarn, twist and plait,
cross them over and over, shape them

into shawls and veils, a fichu to be placed
round the neck of a comtesse or a queen.

Bone and ivory bobbins click like needles,
the clink of ships' masts at their mooring, as we link

meshed nets of grenadine across a réseau ground.
Each strip separate to itself, white as flaked ice,

our fingers raw from the prick of holding-pins.
The lark embroiders his song into our intricate work.

Yet the blet of sky darkens. Night cuts the earth
like a whetted blade. I grow afraid, Sisters, I grow so afraid.

POETRY SECOND PRIZE

MARK FIDDES

'The division of labour in pin manufacturing'

I would have advised him against the ghost grey suit.
Camouflaging yourself as a dead person is not the look.
A male job hunter must appear spry and spear-worthy.
The tie is a sword-penis, the briefcase a box of miracles.
But he's lap-topped himself off for the day in a local café.
He's even using their plug socket. This provides cake power.
Not real power. His charts will sink and flop like sponge.
His smile will decay. He will walk as a teaspoon among men.
Nobody writes a killer pitch on a Happy Baguette napkin.
Pretending to work only makes you good at pretending.
When the family find out, he will become a jellyfish to them.
The tearful eyes, that's only for footballers when they win.
They are specialists in success and that makes crying OK.
He is a specialist in weakness and that smells like hot milk.
He no longer travels braced between bodies at rush hour.
Soon he will lose muscle tone, not to be trusted with the frail.
Pets will chew him like he was a toy man made of rubber
With a squeak and detachable parts that can choke a toddler.
He must return to work before his life loses interest in him.
He must visit a cashpoint to withdraw a sharp new £20 note.
He must kneel before it and kiss the profile of Adam Smith.
1723 – 1790. *The division of labour in pin manufacturing*
(and the great increase in the quantity of work that results)
He must do this every day until work is beautiful again.
Until his next job is a magic mountain with views to die for.

POETRY THIRD PRIZE

JULIA DEAKIN

'How can I tell if the bluebells in my garden are Spanish?'

They will be more flamboyant – their skirts flouncier,
more shades of blue plus pinks and whites,
their leaves broader, glossier.

They will sway more rhythmically
at the hint of a breeze, and toss their heads.
At the drum of a woodpecker, listen: one of them
will start to stamp.

They won't eat till nearly midnight
and then will go clubbing till four, long after their English cousins
are in bed.

When not dancing they will win Wimbledon,
build high speed trains and fantastic cathedrals.
They will save their broken plates to make mosaics.

On warm summer nights they will stroll
en familia through the parks and tree-lined squares,
the young talking phones and mopeds.
They will be in two minds about animal rights.
The grandmothers will remember Franco.

The men will sit in bars eating octopus, discussing
Gareth Bale.

Their tearaways will get roadside shrines.

Complete strangers – bluebells you hardly know
will say *hola* to you.

MATT BARNARD

Eel

Dark river of itself, curled in the bottom of the creel
the small myth was an absence, a light taker,
pulsing with malevolence, its oily body slick
with power and potential, head, tail, middle
a single unremitting story told to the end.

None would put his hand in, tempt the malicious eye
or risk springing the trap of its jaws. Even it's name,
the mysterious double e, defied us, bled sound.
Neither fish nor animal, we knew elvers would cross
fields and roads to reach the sea. Could he be a god?

Three days they forget about him in the bucket.
He baked in the sun, skin drying brown,
contemplating the distant blue of the sky,
until one took pity and brought him down to the sea
uncurled his body and with tender fingers

sluiced the water through his gills.
How it must have felt, the prisoner released
into the light, Houdini cheating the burning rope -
the thin triumphant smile, the vengeful gleam,
before he disappeared into the blackness of himself.

TOM COLLINGRIDGE

British Bulldog

From the first floor window, I watch them playing
British Bulldog. It doesn't work anymore:
If you're caught, you've got to accept it.

But half the kids deny point blank that they were tagged,
As if the lad on 'it' were a store detective.
They laugh off his frustrations and jog on.

But they're bored before they've even reached the far wall
And start looking round,
Hungry for something else to get away with.

That girl again. Leaning against the playground's only tree,
Popping gum, creating distance. Right now, her dad
Is in the pub. Resentful, sullen, pissed,

Despairing. I get an image of last night, him giving her
A sudden slap for some casual lip. For a second
She's shocked, but after that she's unsurprised.

The bell goes to remind me that I made this up.
I've never met her father, don't even know her name. Yet...
I'm new here, I spend my time telling people.

I turn back to my class of bright ones. They're looking up,
A few worried frowns. I hope my smile is reassuring. Anyway,
We turn briskly to page 39 and what we're good at.

KEN EVANS

How Not to See Bears

A butterfly opens and shuts on petals of Indian Paint Brush
the colour of burnt shoulders. A waterfall topples
over Alberta firs. The stream cools by sound alone.

The Parks' Advice is clear:
Walk in groups of four or more. Talk to let them know
you're near.

The forest floor is pine damp, animated by midges. Thirty steps off
a bear brakes on her haunches, recoils
on furred, hydraulic legs, a dense animal stockade.

The Parks' Advice is simple:
Say 'Hey bear!' Use a low soothing voice. Lift your walking poles, look
non-aggressive.

She lifts her head, sniffs our insignificance. For three tall seconds
her cinnamon ruff shakes pollen from a moist snout. She has our heat,
our beating sides. Birds unstick themselves from trees.

The Parks' Advice is stark:
Make yourself big with rucksacks. Retreat slowly, don't make
eye contact.

We tread backwards, damned by snapping twigs, the roll of rocks.
That quivering snout out of sight, we run, white-watering on adrenaline,
crash through bush, gash legs on logs, join a silence of brown needles.

Fresh rain drips from wild raspberries. Moss squelch under boots.
That noise we bend to hear, alert as bugs, is
not her stamping feet, but our hearts seeking a back way out of a ribcage.
The Parks' Advice is harsh:

if a defensive attack, fight back; if aggressive,
play dead.

Water cuts down rock, sluices over, churns to a sound
not her. Pause, listen: it builds, climbs down, turns into wet tyres
swishing rain on tarmac, a silver shot of SUV cuts between spruce.

Reprieve, road. We flag the next car coming, apologise
for bloodying their baby-seat, dirty boots on their picnic-cooler.
We giggle at their chatter, wonder at beautiful faces in the dark.

IAN HARKER

Auntie Lois Astonishes Us All

We are perched at all angles around the living room
with plates of quiche and crisps and cupfuls and cupfuls of wine
when Auntie Lois makes her revelation – her husband,
Uncle Howard, has been alive all this time and she's keeping him
in the greenhouse, his size fives – his delicate, elaborate,
perfectly realised size fives in a bag of compost sprinkled neatly
with woodchip bark.

Auntie Lois is ninety-four. For twenty years we have been fearing
the onset of dementia, dreading the day when Auntie Lois,
who went to keep fit until she was eighty-seven,
should start going gaga, start losing her marbles.
This is it, we think, as Lois leads us down the garden path
to the greenhouse – really a lean-to – and fishes out the key
from among the tissues in her cardigan pocket.

Sure enough Uncle Howard is stood at the sunny end
of the greenhouse surrounded by plant pots and bird feeders
and rusty trowels. 'Here he is,' Lois announces
and here he is, my great uncle Howard right as rain
with his bare feet in a bag of compost. No one knows what to say.

'His hair wants cutting.' Lois brushes his hair back
over his ears. 'I have to go easy on the Baby Bio.'
Dad plucks up courage. 'You alright, Uncle Howard?'
Howard smiles and nods. He seems very happy.
'He takes a lot of looking after,' Auntie Lois says,
filling a watering can from the tap under the clematis.
'Fellas always take a lot of looking after.'

MICHAEL DERRICK HUDSON

Drunk in Bed Playing with an Empty Antique Revolver

Yippee for annihilation. I press home the muzzle's tiny
cool zero against my skull's delicate crock

of cherry preserves. Such theatrics! *Bravo! Encore!*

squeal the critics. But my whatchamacallit soul needs
a kick in the pants, that drowsy old shirker

(chickenshit as always) napping away
the years in the sticky basement of my pineal gland...

Click. Click. God should be here for this, a shimmery
golden nimbus with a silver Santa beard

to grant me three wishes, a fairy godmother of sorts

who'd demolish with her star-spangled wand decades
of tangles and plaque: my girl-unbuttoning

X-ray specs, my adamantine bullet-proof chest-protector
and matching Iron Helmet of a Thousand

Nefarious Excuses. She'd deaccession the five-volume
edition of my *Collected Protocols and Inversions*,

my redacted batch of letters to Miss Busch (illustrated

with blanched, well-thumbed visuals) and
that script about my boyhood duck-n-cringe (optioned

but never produced). Then she'd forgive my jittery
regrets, these flubdubs and repeated

nocturnal pulls on the trigger. But I promise, no blam-
blams. No cops in the bedroom spritzing

the headboard for spatter. No farewells or cruel world

inventories. No sir, not tonight. Just me
and an old hammer on another empty chamber dropped.

LIZ LEFROY

Michelangelo's David

I didn't plan for this, queueing with my sons,
i miei figli, for the Galleria dell'Accademia
to see Michelangelo's David.
We're in Florence, *Firenze*, Italy, *Italia.*
I've brought no food, no drink, no pack of cards,
niente, not even an Italian phrasebook.

Half an hour and just ten feet along it's:
'Whose idea was this?' and the danger of feeling
this queue's a mistake we needn't have started.
But, given time, we become more fluent,
take it in turns to drift in and out to buy *focaccia,*
pizza, tre gelati, un cappuccino, limonata, acqua,
discover we've learnt these words without trying.

It turns out this is why we are waiting:
for loose-limbed time leaning on walls,
leaning on each other, playing with words,
playing with our hair, making it up as we go along.
We're unsure of the scope but discover that love
can be translated into time in any language.
David's the perfect excuse for being here
in Florence in the sun on a Wednesday in April –
for trying out being together in Italian.

I miei figli, *i miei cari figli*, my beloved sons:
this is, after all, my point. Passing time with you
is all, *tutto,* enough, *basta*. And look, *guarda!*
Even our shadows are smiling.

HELEN PARIS

How to Save a Singer

Avoid the throat, keep her upright,
don't let the water spill into her lungs.
If it does you must hold her, rock her gently
so the vibrato of the water plays down the length of her larynx.

Keep her mouth open, keep her singing.
If she has forgotten the words
offer temporary replacements,
soothing vowels, soft images:

soup
swoop
sweet
spoon.

Lay her down on her side to sing a sliding scale.
Stroke her gently
from her neck to her shoulder blade
easing the notes on their way.

Weight her down, distract her,
pour red wine into the pools of her collarbones
fill them to the brim,
beseech her to hum the aromatic notes:

burnt cherry
dark fruit
deep tannin
ripe berry.

C. E. J. SIMONS

The Kung Fu Master's Résumé

The kung fu master looked over his résumé:
his startup had just gone belly-up or
face-down on a thousand pounds of new practice mats;
the lines of credit were cut; the staff in an uproar—

hadn't they heard there was a recession on?
But you have to look out for number one,
and he was the entrepreneur: 'Death Fist, Inc.'
was his baby. The fun was over, but it *had* been fun,

and he'd always kept his head up, even when the others sank.
So what next for the boss man, the *sifu*, the *sensei*,
now that he'd packed up his swords and his sparring pads
and taken down the poster warning, 'Preparation is the Best Defence'?

He sat in his office one last time,
surrounded by the piled corpses of the company accounts,
and read through his résumé, weighing his options,
trying not to think about which of his cheques would bounce.

It was a brilliant résumé, but would they believe it?
Or would they find his achievements a touch—abstract?
Created a workforce of invulnerable men and women—
Remodelled head office to withstand ninja attacks—

And what about his skill set? Did it lack relevance?
Can punch through a block of reinforced concrete—
Can turn the strength of multiple opponents against them—
Can stand on his hands and fight with his feet—

Would they say he needed to 'diversify his experience'?
No, he'd read *Fortune* magazine—his skill set would impress them.

Shows no mercy in competition—every CEO had that one,
the same goes for *Trains employees and customers to obey without question*.

Some doubts circled like assassins, but he fought them off,
like the nightmare of the only interview question he feared:
'What is it you can actually *do*?' In dreams, he gave an honest answer:
I can get out of anyone's way—and then hit them really hard.

He had a degree in physics—once thought he'd go into finance—
or something to do with computers—something profitable.
But a hobby became a career: the sweat-stink, the locked gazes,
and the thrill of the thud as someone else took the fall.

JAMES STRADNER

manta ray poem

The giant manta ray moves like a bed being made.
It is one of the pancakes that Evolution has flipped out.

Imagine manta rays swimming together
like a flock of magic carpets.

When food is scarce they photosynthesise like leaves.
Fact!
Once on a boat in the Med
I saw a group of them hanging on the skin of the water,
lily-pads feasting on daylight.
They slipped down to the seabed as we approached.

Now a diver is cutting away at the wire wrapped around
one that has got stuck
and the fleshy disc body hangs vertically, flexing,
making the edges of itself ripple.
It is hanging patiently,
patiently a thinking thing,
trying not to move.

EOGHAN WALLS

Kraken Rising

The ink-sac bursts. I hold it up to let my daughter see,
flour the rings, fry them and plate up deep-fried squid.

That night she wakes screaming about the dead squid,
whether it hurts being dead, and if she really has to die.

I tell her great nets of squid will wash onboard and die,
so fishermen bring money home at the end of the night.

I lift her to the window to see the wide Sardinian night
naming the Big Dipper, the North Star and Andromeda.

I tell her life is massive; how Perseus saved Andromeda
unchaining her just in time to hang her name on a galaxy.

I tell of supernovas and light and that even a dead galaxy
is bright for centuries; we swim in the cells and dreams

of kids and lovers when we die. But she is lost to dreams,
and I feel like Cephus as he turned from the bubbling sea.

SHORT STORY FIRST PRIZE

JUDITH EDELMAN

Ping at the Zoo

Ack, ack, ack! say New Mother and New Father. Ping blinks up at them. They are taking her someplace. New Mother has laid out Ping's new red coat and blue mittens, her fur hat, sleek as her own hair. She wears shoes with straps and buckles; they look like still black water, they are so glossy. New Father has drawn pictures for her: animals she knows, monkeys and birds and cats, and animals she doesn't, big dark shapes, some with horns and tails and some with orange hair like New Mother's. The animals are behind bars.

New Father points to the pictures and says something that sounds like he is trying to speak Chinese, but it is wrong, so she doesn't know what he is saying. New Mother and New Father do not speak Chinese and Ping does not speak English. When they talk, they sound to her like noisy birds that cannot sing: Ack, ack, ack. Like crows.

***

When Ping was born, she didn't make a sound, but slipped into this world like a ripe plum falling softly into the grass by its tree. Her mother, Meifen, gathered her wet, purple daughter to her and called her Ping. Peaceful.

Her husband said, Small is more like it. Call her Miao Xiao.

Miao Xiao. Insignificant.

Don't worry, he said, we'll keep trying.

***

Ping walks between New Mother and New Father, holding their big hands. She is little, though she is a girl of eight. Wen Li, her favorite caretaker, said that she was born small and will always be small, though the food at the orphanage was good and they tried to feed her enough.

When she first saw New Mother and New Father in a hotel in China, where the caretakers brought her to meet them, she thought they were giants! She kicked and cried because of a story one caretaker used to tell of a giant who stole children and locked them in a gold chest and took them out one by one to fill his stomach when it was empty.

Ping asked Wen Li what she had done wrong that she was being given away to giants and Wen Li told her she was being silly and pushed her into New Mother's arms. Ping went limp then, because sometimes if you play dead, her friend Suyin said, you won't get eaten. Giants, she said, like their children alive and fresh. Ping tried to play dead the whole trip to America. She didn't look at them, she didn't eat, lay as still as she could. New Mother cried. Once she got to America, though, Ping realized that everyone here is a giant. They do not seem to eat children. She prefers not to make a sound, though. Just in case.

New Mother is dressed in a long coat made of animal skin. She wears boots with high heels, and gold on her fingers, on her ears and around her neck. She walks like beautiful women walk in China – proud, graceful, swaying like willow trees in the wind – but she has puffy orange hair and spots all over her face. If Ping looked like that, her caretakers would have hidden her away forever. Her parents would have given her away sooner.

New Father gives money to a man in a booth and they push through a gate to enter the park. It smells like one hundred orphanage bathrooms. Ping wrinkles her nose and New Mother laughs. She often laughs, or cries, and Ping doesn't know why. New Father is more serious, but she is more afraid of him. His eyebrows hang so low, you can't see the color of his eyes, except when he looks right at you, and then you see they are blue and they make you shiver. When he raises his voice at New Mother, he doesn't sound like a crow, but like the roaring trucks on the wide street outside the orphanage. She thinks black smoke wants to come out of his mouth.

New Mother buys something puffy on a stick and hands it to Ping. It looks like New Mother's hair, except pink. New Father and New Mother are watching her. She doesn't know what to do, so she just holds the stick. New Mother pulls off some of the pink hair and puts it in her mouth. Strands stick to her lips. Ping pulls a tiny bit off and tastes it. It dissolves in her mouth, but is so sweet, her tongue burns. She shakes her head and gives it back. New Mother laughs again. New Father pats Ping's hat.

This is not the first strange food they have given Ping. The kitchen New Mother cooks in is white like the bathroom and the food she makes is often white, too, and bland, like tofu, but she does not put a nice brown sauce with red chilies and ginger on it. Sometimes, it smells like feet. Ping thinks they don't know about all the good flavors of food. Right this minute, she wants to taste the black spice that numbs and the red spice that heats, the dumplings filled with meat, and the crunchy pickled vegetables in the morning congee. Here when she wakes up, they give her a bowl of tiny, hard, sweet dumplings floating in milk from a cow, which go quickly soggy.

They walk along paths lined with trees whose leaves have just started to pop out. There are many people, though not so many as on any street in X—. They make their way past cages of monkeys, and Ping sees this is a zoo. The caretakers sometimes took the orphans to F— Park on warm days, but never to the zoo, though there is one in X—. Ping didn't realize animals live in cages at the zoo; she thought they walked around their park free, like pigeons or ducks.

The monkeys scream at the people and at each other; they swing on the bars and hang from their tails. Children are pointing at them and laughing as if the monkeys are funny, but Ping thinks the monkeys are angry, the way they shriek.

New Father and New Mother seem excited. Ping's legs work hard to keep up with their long steps as they pull her along between them. They come to a cage surrounded by lots of people and a long line waiting to see whatever is inside. People do not push to the front the way they do in X—. People here do not like to be too near strangers, but New Mother and New Father and their friends like to hug and kiss and touch each other and Ping. She does not like their big faces against hers, their breath on her skin, their lips on her cheeks, the way they pet her black hair as though she were a house cat. They touch the people they know as if they were all little children needing hugs and kisses. Ping is a grown girl and doesn't need that.

The house of New Mother and New Father is big enough for twenty orphans, but she is alone in her room and has a hard time sleeping without Suyin and Jie and the other girls in their beds near hers. If she wraps herself in the blankets very tightly and tells herself one of the stories she knows, as though she were listening to Suyin whisper to her in the dark, it is a little easier to fall asleep. Suyin is the one who told Ping about what happens when you get a new family.

Americans are rich, she said. You live in a house like the G— Palace with many friends and brothers and sisters and they dress you in green silk and you eat meat dumplings all day and you never have to clean the bathroom.

That's a lie, Jie said. You are like a servant, cleaning and cooking and working every minute.

Suyin told Jie she was just jealous that Ping was going to go live with New Mother and New Father. She turned to Ping. Who are you going to believe, me or jealous Jie? You can tell them to take me, too.

Don't you want a nice new family? the caretakers said.

***

Three years passed and one miscarriage, then a boy, born too early, who died in his father's hands. There's still time, he said. Pray for a brother, he told Ping.

Meifen ate red-painted eggs and taro, though she had a new aversion to both. They gave all their neighbors – the ones they shared the house with, the ones in other houses – lanterns and clay dolls, good omens for a son, though they could not afford the gifts. When she got pregnant again, she did not think the pregnancy would last. Her husband was especially kind and careful: he would not let her eat rabbit or ginger.

It was as though the baby fought to get out and Meifen's body fought to keep him in. She thought she would be rent in two when he crowned. Holding him felt like dying, she loved him so much. As she loved Ping. The same. Different.

***

Finally, it is Ping's turn to see the animal. New Mother is pointing and chattering like a monkey and New Father lifts Ping up to look. She sees bamboo, long swaying green clusters of it, which she hasn't seen since she left X—. Then she sees the bears. Pandas. Every child in China knows them. There are two. They are quiet and shy; one of them keeps his back turned on the people. They eat their bamboo and do not make a sound.

New Father puts Ping down and he and New Mother are pointing at her and then at the pandas. Ping, the pandas, back and forth. She thinks they are telling her that she is like the pandas. You are both from China, she thinks they mean, and you are both shy and quiet. It seems to make New Father and New Mother very happy to think about Ping and the pandas together, as though they were reuniting her with her best friend, Suyin.

She is not like the pandas, except that they both live far away from their friends and the places they know. Ping is from a city; these pandas are from a forest she's never seen. The pandas do not look happy exactly, but they look like they are quiet on the inside as well as quiet on the outside. Ping is quiet on the outside.

Her mother used to praise her for being quiet. Your father is sleeping, she said. Be silent as a smooth stone. When you do speak, let it sound like water trickling over.

Whenever her father was at home, he was tired. Her mother said the factory wrung him out like a rag. He did not have much to say to Ping, except what a little thing she was, as though he were surprised every time he saw her. Help your mother, he said.

Ping helped make the congee, and hang the wash, and while her mother grew big with Ping's brother, she taught Ping how to fold the squares of dumpling dough around the meat, how to pinch them so they did not fall apart in the pot, how to keep the broth just chuckling. Ping wished then they could have dumplings every day, instead of rice with cabbage. Now she wishes she had rice and cabbage.

Ping turns her back on the pandas. New Mother drops Ping's hand. Her face is turning pink and her rock-colored eyes are watering. The black makeup she puts on her eyelashes to make them look like spiders is starting to drip down her face like dirty rain. New Father puts his arm around her shoulders. She buries her face in his chest. They hold each other as though someone has died. Ping walks away.

***

At Three Mornings, the men drank their cups of *maotai* and the women fussed over the new son. Meifen kept Ping close to her, would not let her wander among the celebration's guests, as though she thought one of them might spirit her away while Meifen's gaze was elsewhere.

The guests had left and Ping was asleep when Meifen's husband said, There is no money for two.

I will find more work, she said.

There will not be enough. Do you want to take food out of our son's mouth?

Why don't you just kill us both then?

He held her arms to steady her shaking. Someone will take her, he said.

***

No one notices Ping in her red coat, maybe because everyone here dresses in bright colors or maybe because there is so much to see. In places without animals to stare at, like stores or buses, people stare at Ping. The sun is warm and Ping does not need her mittens anymore, so she puts them in her pocket.

She is calmer inside, disappearing among the legs and bundled up bodies, the sticky-faced children, the stands with people selling toy animals and bright balloons, the too-sweet sticks of melting hair in pink and blue, long sausages on buns, and the smells of animals and food whirl together in her nose, not unpleasant anymore, and just looking at people's shoes and clothes, not their faces, it is like she is walking down C— Street with the other children, their caretakers herding them towards F— Park where it is Spring and blossoms burst open on the trees, the wind blowing their sweet smell into the children's faces, and they run through the showers of pink and white petals falling in their hair and brushing against their cheeks like cool fingers.

Ping walks past a mirror, stops. Not a mirror, a face like hers on a boy in a red sweater. He is only a little taller than she is, so maybe they are the same age. The mother and father holding his hands also look Chinese. She says hello to the boy. She says, are you visiting here, too? He stares at Ping and looks up at his parents. When they open their mouths, they sound like everyone else here. It is awful to her to hear those crow sounds coming out of Chinese faces.

It is like the morning she woke before the sun to hear her quiet mother screaming. Their neighbor, Mrs. Chiang, was there when Ping sat straight up in her bed in the corner of the kitchen. Sshh, she said, it is only your brother arriving. Ping hid under her blanket. For hours, Ping's brother made her mother weep and yell, and when he finally arrived, he screamed as though he were the one being hurt. Mrs. Chiang brought him out wrapped up like a dumpling. He was the ugliest thing Ping had ever seen: toothless, red and wrinkled, a few black hairs pasted to his peanut-shaped head. *I won't love him*, she thought.

The strangers are still talking to Ping, and their stupid boy is staring, so she turns back into the stream of legs and lets it carry her away. She will never learn to make those sounds; she'd rather never speak again.

Ping does not feel like she is in F— Park anymore. The crowd's voices crash into the cries of the animals and make her ears hurt. Flashy birds scold her. Lazy gray beasts snort from their mud pits. Monkeys without tails who look like ugly children shake the bars and throw things, baring their teeth. These animals are so angry or sad or crazy, they fling themselves against their cages and shout.

They were tricked. If she had the strength of a giant, she would tear open these bars and the animals would run or fly back to their forests and skies and water. What if they don't know how to get there? Maybe they don't even remember where they came from it's been so long.

Ping is no giant. Maybe she *is* like the pandas, eating what is placed in their cage, silently turning away.

***

There were no childless aunts, no neighbors to step in. Some already had one girl and prayed daily for a boy; they envied Meifen her good fortune. Others already had their boy; they observed how skinny her children were, how much the baby boy cried; they pitied her misfortune.

Mrs. Chiang said, Quick is kind.

Her husband said, I will do it.

Meifen kept her face still, but something blew through her, like a terrible wind out of season that tears the blossoms from the fruit trees and pummels them rotten on the ground. It stirred up wild thoughts. She would take her children and run. (She had no money. No one would take her in.) She would kill them both and herself. (She looked at their tender bodies and thought she must weep at the evil thought.) She would scratch her husband's eyes out, fight like a wild animal. (Why did he not love Ping?)

No, she said. I will do it.

He placed his palm on her head, as though laying a blessing upon it. Do it soon.

***

The sun yawns hot upon Ping and the top of her head feels like it is burning, though the rest of her is cold. Her empty stomach croaks. She wonders what the monkeys are eating.

She ate all her rice and was very quiet her last day at home, because she knew her mother was taking her someplace. She'd laid out Ping's traveling clothes and Ping was excited because that meant they weren't just going to the market or to Mrs. Chiang's house. Maybe they would go into the city, just the two of them. Maybe they would shop and eat noodles. It had been a long time since they'd eaten anything but rice. Sometimes, her mother didn't even eat that, but gave Ping her share. Then her father would yell at her mother that she would have no milk for Ping's brother if she didn't eat.

Today, Ping had thought, they would sit on stools in the shop window and draw pictures with their fingers in the steam from the noodle pots. Ping stood up on a stool at the basin and began to wash her bowl and spoon by herself to show her mother that although she was only five, she was old enough to help her mother pick out the best spices and carry the bags with their shopping in them. She would not complain no matter how tired she got.

Ping let a cloth fall over her brother in his cradle next to the basin. His moon face disappeared. Her mother might forget he was there and they would wait for the bus together and get on it and be far into the city before she remembered him. By then it would be too late to go back for him, so she would say, oh well, and they would slurp their noodles and laugh.

Ping's bowl was slippery; it fell out of her hands and broke. Her mother spoke sharply and her brother began to cry and she knew her mother would not take her into the city now, so Ping began to cry, too. But she was wrong. Her mother stopped scolding and put her hands on Ping's cheeks as though Ping's face were broken like the bowl and she was putting it back together, but it was her mother's face that looked like it was breaking. There were cracks in it that did not go away when she smiled at Ping.

She dressed Ping in her heavy blue tunic and pants, though she had been dressing herself for a long time, and tied Ping's brother to her chest, and they walked down the road to meet the bus. Her mother had taught Ping the trick of picking up her feet and putting them down carefully when she walked, to raise as little dust as possible. Ping made sure not to shuffle her black slippers at all, so when they got to the city, her clothes had very little dust on them from their dirty road.

***

The minutes passed like no time: the washing, the cooking, stretching their money to meet their last need which it never did, and the children (the children) occupied her hands and mind, and she seemed to have no feeling in either, and when her husband lost his factory job, they lived only on rice and cabbage, then rice alone, and the children did not grow and her breasts dried up, and a day came, an ordinary day (a broken bowl, the baby fussing, the fine brown dust that *would* get in, no matter how often she swept) that was, at the same time, the end of the world, and she passed through it as though passing over it, thinking, *this is what it is like to be dead*, and saw how Ping lifted her careful feet like a cat as they went to catch the bus into the city.

***

Ping's fur hat has slipped off her head and is hanging down her back by its ties. Her hands are cold, so she stops to put her mittens back on, but they have fallen out of her pocket and are nowhere around. New Mother and New Father will be angry she lost her new mittens. New Father will yell at her and her hands will be cold. She thinks she will hunt for her mittens, but then she looks up into the cage she is standing in front of and a dozen frogs hop in her stomach, for a pair of huge yellow eyes is watching her!

These eyes are the gold of the J—Temple Buddha. They can see through Ping's red coat into her skinny body. They see her heart banging against her chest like a monkey in a cage. They see her family, the orphanage, New Mother and New Father, the room she sleeps in alone, the mittens she lost. The gold eyes burn like candles and they live in a black face, the face of a great cat, not like the cats who roam and scratch in the orphanage alley, mewing for food. This is a Cat God. Ping feels as though she knows a story about this god, but has not heard it yet.

On the bus, her mother told her a story of a rabbit who grew too big for his hole. People pressed up against their knees. Her brother on her mother's chest blinked at everything, but looked like he was too stupid to know what he was seeing.

Rabbit started small but grew and grew, Ping's mother said, till parts of him poked out of the ground. Animals would trip over his foot sticking up, and once, a mouse nibbled on an ear, thinking it was a plant.

Her brother's toes peeked out from his swaddling. Ping pinched the big one hard when her mother was looking out the window. He squawked and began to cry.

Her mother soothed him and said, Rabbit grew more and more uncomfortable, forced into a hole too small for him. Then Rooster came by and asked why he did not leave the hole. I like this hole, Rabbit said. But Rooster saw that he was in pain in the little hole and told him it was time to find a bigger one. I can't get out, said Rabbit. Rooster pecked and pecked the ground around Rabbit until he was free.

Ping loosened the end of the blanket tucked around her brother. When they got up, maybe the blanket would fall open and he would tumble to the floor of the bus and they could leave him there. Maybe someone would pick him up or maybe he would die.

She doesn't want you, Ping whispered to him.

***

The people flowing down C— Street towards the park could see right through her, Meifen thought. They saw her shriveled nut heart, which nonetheless was hurling itself against her chest like an insane person in a cell. She flinched over and over, as if all those eyes were throwing stones at her.

Meifen circled one block with Ping three times before sitting with her on the steps of an old grey building, as if to rest. Wait right here, she told Ping. Don't move. Watch this bag. You will have dumplings later.

Noodles! said Ping.

Yes, Meifen said, moving away. She watched Ping glue herself to the step, stilling every wiggle of her five-year-old body, determined to deserve noodles. Meifen hid in the shadows across the street. Breathless, mute, she watched the door: closed, closed, still closed. It opened with a gasp: her own. As if she'd finally wrenched it open herself. She watched Ping refuse to go in, shake her head, over and over, as the women coaxed her. She watched her wait and wait and wait, until Ping fell asleep against her bag and the women picked her up and took her inside. Meifen watched the closed door until it disappeared into the dark, the whimpering baby hanging from her hollow chest.

***

The Cat God's fur looks like Ping's hair, slippery and black. You can see his shoulders and legs and chest, all of him, sliding around under his dark coat. You know he is strong; he is powerful! His claws are long and sharp: if you make him angry, he will slice you into a million pieces. He opens his mouth in a roar with no sound. If he wanted, he could scream so loud your ears would fall off. His teeth could sink into your body as if it were tofu. He is prowling a path on the concrete floor of his cage – away from

Ping, back to Ping, away from her – but his eyes never leave her face. He is quiet. On the outside. Inside you can tell he is exploding. His eyes are not candles; they are the flames of a house burning to the ground. His heart is on fire!

Ping wants to point to him, then to herself, him, herself, to show New Mother and New Father the truth they don't see. Ping and the Cat God are brother and sister, separated and brought back together. The Cat God sees that Ping's heart is not a monkey in a cage, but a terrible fire.

This is why New Mother and New Father took her from China. Wen Li said it was her destiny. She had not understood why she did not have a different destiny, a destiny in which her brother was never born and she stayed with her mother and father, and never looked upon the strange faces of New Mother and New Father, never had to eat their tasteless food, or sleep by herself, or hear the songful sound of Chinese only in her own head. Now she knows.

Other people look over the hedge at the Cat God, watch for a few seconds and walk away to other cages. He is so quiet on the outside, people do not notice him. No one sees. Ping reaches up and grasps a clump of stiff hedge. It is thorny, but she holds on. Her hands sting, but she pulls herself up.

Ping! she hears. Ping! Ping!

Far away, New Mother and New Father run, pushing people out of their way. New Father is waving her blue mittens.

Ping scrambles and kicks; thorns catch on her coat and her tights, scratch at her hands and face. Her hair blows up and around in the spring wind. It is like a thousand black snakes hissing.

The Cat God stops pacing to watch Ping, bleeding from a hundred scratches, struggle up the hedge. He lowers his head and waits for her. Ping stretches a hand to him; she can almost touch the bars. Her name multiplies in the air. It is bird noise in her ears, so consumed is she by the story of what happens next: *Ping lets the Cat God inside out. She screams the fire high and she is mighty for all to see. She tears open the bars and jumps on the Cat God's back. Ping's hair and the Cat God's tail blow behind them as they leap the hedge-the people-the park-the world home.*

A hand yanks Ping's foot and she loses her grip. The eyes of the Cat God, twin comets, follow her down as she drops, roaring, into New Mother's arms.

***

When Ping fell into this world like a ripe plum from its tree, Meifen gathered her up and turned away from the midwife trying to take the baby from her.

To clean her, said Mrs. Chiang.

The new mother held her off, one bare arm arched over Ping like a curving branch.

SHORT STORY SECOND PRIZE

JOHN HOBART

Mannington May Be Mad

The first time it happened, Jones woke with a start and gasped out, 'Yes?' But there was no reply. And when he opened the door, warily, knowing this could be nothing but an emergency, knowing this could only be something that would ask for backbone, there was nobody there. There was only the darkness of the corridor, and the closed door of Mannington's room. He stood with his heart hectic and his understanding stumped, the absence before him as strange as that caused by a conjuror, and there came a point when he began to wonder if those two sharp knocks had, in fact, belonged to the end of a dream rather than to the start of what was so, if there hadn't been a moment of overlap between the sleeping realm and the waking, and he'd been fooled into ludicrous alarm. But they'd had such solidity, those knocks, had had such a lot of wood in them and such a lot of knuckle. He considered Mannington's door. It could only have been Mannington, couldn't it. But it was hard to believe that Mannington would have done such a thing. Would have rapped on his door in the middle of the night and then snuck away. With a spiteful snicker, say, relishing the thought of his perplexity. He didn't, it was true, know Mannington well, and there had, of late, been a little tension between them. But that had had the most trivial cause and couldn't, surely, have given rise to this. For several minutes he stood there, confounded, attending to the stillness of the flat. Mannington's door disclosed nothing. There it was, across the way. And behind it Mannington either guiltlessly slept or maliciously listened.

He said nothing of it, Jones, the next day. He heard Mannington in the passage but baulked at the complication of an encounter. It was a largely carpetless flat, old and cold and solid, with a predominance of uncushioned wood, and its bareness made Mannington's movements distinct. He listened to Mannington's frank heels on the floorboards and to the clinking clarity of Mannington's teaspoon, turning its circles within Mannington's cup of tea. It had had a severity, the knocking, that smacked of Mannington. For there really wasn't much give in Mannington. There was, for example, something taut about his wardrobe – his trim trousers, his tidy ties. It had the orderliness, his way of dressing, of a man who had been in the military. But no, that wasn't quite right. It suggested not a man who had been in the military, but a man who would pretend to have been.

It happened again, the knocking, the very next night. Again he woke to it. And again, when he went to the door – quickly, very quickly, to catch the ridiculous Mannington in the act – there was nobody there. This really made him very uncertain. It was possible, he knew, that the knocking was a nonsense, a noise belonging to the final second of his sleep. He had looked it up, this phenomenon. It existed. It wasn't uncommon. But it was also possible that there, a mere six feet away, stood Mannington, revelling, malevolently, in his bafflement, having embarked on a programme of persecution. Though the disappearance of Mannington's chocolate had really had nothing to do with him. He suspected Mannington had, at some point, miscounted his bars or, the last time he had consumed one, had failed to mentally make the subtraction and was working from a laggardly tally. But Mannington had reacted badly to that idea. And he had got a glimpse of the fact, at that point, that to ever charge Mannington with a mistake was to enter a battle. He was in his late forties, probably, Mannington, and disquietingly devoid of friends.

It was after that second occurrence that he spoke to Mannington, very diplomatically, of the knocking, merely inquiring if he'd heard a noise in the night. But Mannington's affronted stare made it clear that he considered even this careful query critical, and it was necessary to quickly suggest that the disturbance had its source in the street. That he had been affronted, of course, did not attest to his innocence. Human beings were not so straightforward as that. But it was hard to believe, nevertheless, that the mere loss of a bar of chocolate could have roused the man to this vindictiveness. It would mean that here was a man for whom no blow was small, for whom every graze was an outrage. What he was to this man – it was troubling to think of it. That he might be a figure in a fiction in the mind of a man who seethed, that he might have been plumped up into a fiend by paranoia – this was unsettling. He contemplated an act of propitiation. Making Mannington a gift of chocolate, say. A mollifying amount of chocolate. Three bars. Four. But that might, might it not, be considered a confession of guilt. And he found it difficult, anyway, to imagine Mannington being mollified by anything. Mannington, he imagined, was not a man who needed grounds for bitterness in order to be bitter. He could manage, Jones imagined, exceedingly well without.

That night no knocking occurred. He wondered if his questioning of Mannington had made him think better of his harassment. Perhaps two nights of wrecked sleep, in Mannington's mind, was the proportionate punishment for the theft of a chocolate bar. Things, now, were even. He considered cleaning the bathroom to reinforce the restoration of peace. But he couldn't remember where the cleaning products were kept. It was Mannington who valued cleanliness. He was more often to be seen in washing-up gloves than not. He'd been spotted in those yellow gloves of his, in fact, in circumstances not strictly consistent with sanity. When reading a newspaper. When going to the lavatory. It wasn't clear, on those occasions, whether he'd merely failed to remove the gloves after some chore, or whether the gloves had been specially donned for those deeds, in pursuit, presumably, of unhinged levels of hygiene. To question him on the subject, Jones felt, would be unwise. Mannington, he was beginning to grasp, was a man made hazardous by questions.

It happened again. He woke in the night to two raps of apparently immaculate actuality, raps that banged on the brain as hard as raps that were real. But he didn't, this time, go to the door. He lay there in the dark and imagined Mannington slipping, with practised rapidity, back into his bedroom, grimly gratified by his act of retribution. He would have crept into his bed, wouldn't he, and be feigning sleep, curled up under his sheets in a state of savage glee, a fifty-year-old man engaged in a preposterously petty war. What Mannington's past was he didn't really know. In the few, very constrained conversations they'd had, there'd been no mention of women. Or of men. And very little of work. He was involved, it seemed, in insurance. But it had to be the case, didn't it, that here was a man made sore by a shortfall of respect and rewards. He thought himself wronged. Comprehensively wronged. And now here was a wrong against which he was taking up arms. This, anyway, was the picture of Mannington that was growing in Jones's mind. And Jones, now, was finding it difficult to divert his thinking from the subject, found himself unstillably given to conjectures and to stratagems. Perhaps a replacement bar could be clandestinely added to Mannington's stash. Mannington, of course, would suspect the addition, but perhaps he would also be induced to question the correctness of his counting, be made sufficiently suspicious of his arithmetic that he'd rein in his revenge. But no, Mannington was not a man who would be inclined to question himself. He would have a terrifying amount of trust in his judgement. And besides, to add a bar would require entering Mannington's room, and he was a man of such prickly propriety that only the very intrepid would attempt such a trespass. In fact this, Jones began to think, could account in part for Mannington's anger – the notion that his room had been invaded. His things seen. For his things betrayed, perhaps, something he was ashamed of. A lack of money. A lack of intellect. An undisciplined inclination. Jones had never actually crossed the threshold of Mannington's room, though he had, on a couple of occasions, caught glimpses through the briefly open door and seen nothing that hinted at a shabbiness. A tidy bed. A bedside table. The case for an electric razor. It would be boringly lurid, of course, to imagine that Mannington had something hideous to hide – a scrapbook, say, dedicated to all the murders he was doing. But the knocking was not the work, was it, of a balanced man, and as the nights passed and the campaign continued, Jones began to grow uneasy at the fact that the key to his own bedroom door was missing. He had never bothered with this key in the past. But now that he wanted it, he couldn't find it. One night he tried to wedge his chair beneath the handle, as he had often seen done in films, but found it lacked the necessary height, and he had to make do with just placing the chair, feebly, in the way of the door, in a mere gesture at impediment. But this was silly. Mannington wasn't dangerous. He moved the chair away from the door. Then thought for a while and moved it back again.

Now, ten or eleven days since the knocking began, Jones was still lacking final certainty as to whether it was the work of a disgruntled knuckle, this knocking, or of a misbehaving brain. There were nights when it seemed very real, and nights when it seemed less so. He wondered whether some nights it was real and some nights it wasn't, whether he hadn't started to hallucinate knocking, perhaps, as a consequence of being beset by actual knocks. It was the case, certainly, that people could wake to noises faked by their brains – knocks, door bells, the shouts of long-dead parents. He had read about it. It was there in the literature. But his own brain, surely, would not behave that way. Even given the upheavals of the past year. And perhaps it was this very phenomenon that Mannington was exploiting. He had chosen this particular method of mischief so that, if confronted, he would have a blameless explanation to hand. And of course there wasn't only the knocking. There was also the missing key. Which Mannington, perhaps, had made away with, so as to gain unfettered access to his bedroom, the better to inspect his bin for incriminatory wrappers. He considered asking Mannington about this key. As casually and as unconfrontationally as possible, making clear that his own carelessness lay behind its loss. But Mannington was capable of understanding all questions, no matter how neutral, as accusations, and besides, if he had indeed filched the key, he would hardly let on.

It bothered Jones to be suspected of pocketing that chocolate. It was only a bar of chocolate, but still, the suspicion was soiling. He couldn't, in Mannington's presence, feel completely clean. He found he was keeping out of Mannington's way in order to spare himself his stare. For it was a very staining stare. And in his limited interactions with Mannington, he found himself offering proofs of his rectitude, shoehorning into their talk his kindness to the blind, and the time he stopped a boy tormenting a cat, hoping this principled history of his would eat into Mannington's thesis of theft. But the knocking continued. The punishment, if it was a punishment, went on. And the punishment, if it was a punishment, was clearly exorbitant. Mannington was no longer the purer party. He had revenged himself into the wrong. Which was a notion worth nurturing. For it made it easier, when Mannington looked at him disdainfully, to wriggle out from under the weight of his disdain.

But Jones, now, was knowing moments of real anger. At being harried in this way. One night he sat on the chair by the door for several hours, waiting for Mannington to do his knocking, planning to pounce and catch him with the knocking still fresh on his knuckles, but the knocking, that night, did not occur, and he did have the passing thought that the knocking, so far, had only ever happened as he slept and might indeed, therefore, be an artefact of the waking brain. He didn't want to be unjust to Mannington. He didn't want to be one of those trite types who assumed that every loner was a lunatic, every oddball a monster. He had found himself, for example, wondering whether that electric razor case he'd glimpsed in Mannington's room was, in fact, the case for something else. Binoculars, say. And Mannington spent his evenings priapically spying on any available neighbourhood nudity. This, he knew, was a coarse thought. A thought, almost certainly, that was coarser than what was so. And he wondered, too, whether he had been unfair to Mannington in the matter of the gloves. Perhaps, after all, Mannington had donned the gloves in order to clean the lavatory rather than to use it, and his manual apparel didn't indicate, in any way, some crazed aversion to touching the more intimate elements of his anatomy. It was hard, now, to remember exactly how things had been. But he feared his take on the man was a skewed cartoon and he was interpreting everything Mannington did in that cartoon's falsifying light. He thought again, hard, of the knocking and of his inclination to think Mannington the cause. It was possible, Jones supposed, that his ex-wife's actions, over this last, loathsome year, had led him to think of himself as a man besieged, had made him too quick to attribute warpath ways to those around him. Assault, it was true, was something he had come to expect. He didn't want to mistake a tilt in his thinking for the lay of the land. Nevertheless, it couldn't be denied that Mannington was odd about his chocolate. His obsessive inventorying of his store – that *was* a little odd. And he *had* accused him, pretty much, of a theft that had never happened. It wasn't entirely unreasonable, was it, to suggest that such behaviour might be the mark of a man who could work himself up to a sense of peculiar warrant and think a project of punitive pettiness apt. Besides, sometimes the mean thought was the true thought. And the magnanimous the naïve. It wasn't always a skew in your thinking that made a man a wretch. Sometimes a wretch was what a man was.

There they were again. The two raps. And they really did seem something that was so. They really were very convincing. He stared in the dark in the direction of the door. There the chair's vague shape. There the chair's pathetic protection. It wearied him, that failure to fortify the door with the chair. In films the chair was always a perfect fit, rammed up under the handle with gratifying exactness. But his chair was a good six inches too short. It was a very fatiguing thing to look on, that chair, in all its uselessness. He looked on that chair and saw the fact that he was forty and living in a cold flat with a man he barely knew and could barely stand and who was very probably subjecting him, on a near nightly basis, to a nasty assault. It gave him the sense, that chair, that the things that assailed him could not be contained.

That chocolate. He found himself, Jones, as he pulled his covers tight to his chin, thinking about that chocolate. The fact that Mannington's liking for chocolate had been laid bare – that would bother him. There would be humiliation for him in the exposure of an appetite. In the exposure of the fact that his was a self in some way ruled. And that gave Jones a further thought. Quite what Mannington did in insurance wasn't clear, but he wasn't the boss. He couldn't be. And he would find that incensing. He had a sovereign idea of himself yet a life that kept requiring him to curtsey. In fact Jones, as he lay there, began to wonder whether Mannington actually did work in insurance. Someone that offendable had to have something to hide, and he speculated that Mannington was actually jobless and went out each morning in a pitiful facsimile of employment, spending his days on a bench somewhere, equipped with a lunchbox full of homemade sandwiches, and kicking out, with a curse, at any imprudently optimistic pigeons. Yes, Mannington's idea of dignity would involve the masking of fallibility. He could let no one know of a weakness.

More than once he considered a surveillance camera. For proving the truth of the affair. But there was nowhere plausible to conceal it in the corridor. And if Mannington were to find it – and Mannington would – then extraordinary ructions would ensue. Besides, he couldn't afford such a thing. He thought of the footage that would result, the green images of Mannington going about his baleful business, knocking, obnoxiously, in the night. Or of the empty corridor, and what it would say about his brain. He wondered why it was knocks the waking brain was prone to hear. Knocks, bells, yells. They were sounds, he supposed, by which people were commonly woken. He imagined waking to the sound of his dead mother's yell, that long-ago reveille stored, presumably, in some profound mental niche and available for a mendacious reprise. Such things, he had read, did happen. What a magical mendacity – what a melancholy mendacity – that would be. To know a moment when, because of some errant detonation in the brain, that vanished voice would be heard in all its verity, a school morning solidifying, blissfully, around its sound, all the subsequent years and subsequent tears concealed. And then he would open his eyes. An act which, as time had passed, had become less and less advisable. It put before him such very trying things.

When he met Mannington, now, in the corridor or in the kitchen, he would attempt to infer the truth from his person – from any telltale evasiveness or telltale fatigue. The Mannington engaged in nocturnal annoyance would, presumably, look underslept, for his campaign would mean as much disruption for him, wouldn't it, as for his victim. This hadn't really occurred to Jones before. He wondered whether Mannington set his alarm for his attacks, or just took advantage of any occasional wakefulness. Yes, there could be cost in this, couldn't there, for Mannington. It could be a considerable commitment. But he would hardly be the first attacker who harmed himself as much as he harmed the subject of his attacks. The inspections, anyway, were inconclusive. And sometimes insufficiently surreptitious. Mannington was not a man who could safely be stared at. He was dismally quick to bristle. Though there was nothing very terrible about his appearance. His dark hair, of course, was mostly gone, and it was impossible to imagine his thinking that anything other than a mortification. It was somewhat surprising, in fact, that he hadn't yielded to the lure of a comb-over, smearing those side strands, in ludicrous subterfuge, over the shamefully naked pate. That was the kind of thing that Mannington would do. Jones pictured him in front of his mirror, in humourless experiment, trying, with increasing fury, to persuade his pittance to pass as a plenitude. Mannington, surely, understood everyone's eyes as insults, and the friendliest gaze was grounds for spleen.

One day, when walking near the cathedral, just to take some of the barrenness out of the afternoon, Jones saw a man, over on the other side of the road, charging, furiously, at a pigeon. He was some way off, the man, but surely it was Mannington. Wasn't it? The pigeon fled in a panicked kerfuffle, and the man stalked away towards the bridge, having cleared his path of all avian inconvenience. How nice it would be if that were indeed Mannington, acting in glorious accordance with prediction. Yes, it had to have been Mannington. How it would make him fume, the failure of pigeons to shift at his approach. For Mannington wanted deference that Mannington never got. He wanted to be king of something, Mannington, but couldn't find a something that would succumb. And Jones felt it shoring up, this incident, the notion that the knocking was Mannington's doing. He had been right about the pigeons. He must be right about the knocking. He was very tired, now, from the disruption to his sleep and from the occupation of his thoughts, and it was an increasing inducement, this tiredness, to leave off thinking and let something do as truth.

There, in the kitchen, the clatter of pans. There, in the living room, the two brisk swishes that meant the curtains had been closed. He had a characteristic way of closing the curtains, Mannington, bringing them together with a narked smartness that no one could interpret as love for what lay without. Yes, there was Mannington. There was his tread and there was his tidying and there was his temper. It was a lesson, wasn't it, the knocking, in the fact that he mattered. This fact wasn't one he could get the world to agree with. But he was going to get his thief of a flatmate to agree. *I matter!* Jones imagined him yelling, silently, in his room. *I matter!* It wasn't much of a reach, actually, this conjecture. Jones was prone to the odd muted exclamation himself. Sometimes the muting slipped a little and half a howl got out.

Knock knock. There it was again. *Again*. And the raps had all the definiteness of the door in them, and all the substance of the knuckle.

He strode to the door and opened it as quickly as was consonant with quietness. Nothing. Nothing. Just the dim passage with its dim forms – the side table, the ironing board propped against the wall. He gave Mannington's door grim-lipped consideration. For two or three minutes he stood there, staring at it. Then he moved softly across the passage, knocked twice on the door with raps of surprising violence and flashed back into his room, closing his own door, with soundless care, behind him, and slinking between his sheets, where he lay, breathless and giggling and happier, far happier, than the facts of his life would seem to allow.

SHORT STORY THIRD PRIZE

HELEN MORRIS

LOL

For DB

It was a Tuesday. Warm and spring like. If you were lucky the lilac was out and its sweet scent was drifting like heartbreak on the breeze. And you would, like me, have been hypnotised by the lazy, heavy buzzing of a fat, furry bumble bee, zig zagging between the tight clenched flowers. Having said that, in some places it was still Monday night. So you might have slept through it. And in other places, if you were unlucky, it was bone cold and raining in stinging sheets.

I was already missing you. But I would never let you know that.

The first time. It lasted no more than a minute. Although time a minute and you'll see it's much longer than you expect. Go on. Do it. Do it now. I'll wait for you. I'm not going anywhere.

Don't worry.

Don't be afraid.

Well, not of that, anyway.

Don't be afraid of a minute.

The first time. It was just a row of letters. Of one letter. 'w'. Over and over. Over and over.

I thought it was an error. We all thought it was an error. A mistake. A bug. Our phone, our computer, our laptop, our tablet, playing up. A hardening crumb lodged half under a smooth flat key, from the baguette we'd eaten the day before, while typing a feeble joke to a colleague.

Trying to stave off the soul stealing boredom of another day in the office. Where your baguette filling is the most challenging decision you make. Or maybe it was the spot where we had clumsily spilt some orange juice when we'd caught our shirt sleeve as we went to put the glass down. Or maybe that glitchy touch screen. Dropped on the floor two weeks before. After too much beer in the pub. With Ted. Not the same since.

A normal, human event, in any case. Clumsiness, bad luck, poor judgment. Sorry, Ted.

A human event. Causing 'w' to be typed over and over again. A human event.

Like a baby trying to learn to talk.

Exactly like a baby trying to learn to talk. Exactly.

Then, just as that minute ticked away, just as we were all wiping or shaking or poking, it stopped. The letters disappeared. We all paused. Caught adrift by the suddenness of it. As if we had thought there was another step on the stairs. When there was none. We blinked. And then we carried on and thought nothing of it. How quickly we adapted. How quickly we switched back to normal life. Assuming the crumb had dislodged, the key had lifted clean, the glitch had been smoothed away. And we thought it was fixed. And we thought it was only us. But we were wrong. It wasn't.

It wasn't fixed.

We weren't alone.

It wasn't only us.

Later that night, when it began again, we suddenly remembered that this had happened before. But earlier. And familiarity and surprise wrestled within us. And we stood with our mouths and thoughts slightly ajar. Except for those who had been asleep. They were still with surprise, the crumbs, the juice or the floor. For them it was the first time. But not the last time. It wasn't the last time for any of us.

And all across the world, in a great cascade, people found that it wasn't just them. They were not alone. It was everyone. It was their work colleagues, their mothers, the friend they were catching up with in the smart café with the bored baristas, the girlfriend they were trying to break up with, the potential lover they were desperate to sleep with. But who preferred a different physical type. There was no crumb. No clumsily spilt orange juice. There was no Ted in the pub with the stale tasting nuts.

There was just 'w' over and over again. All that your phone tweeted or texted or showed, was 'w'. On every device across the entire world. 'w'. Over and over. Buses ran. Washing machines churned. Lives began. Lives ended. Sometimes so closely together they both seemed the same. I lost one of the small green earrings Mark had given me when we had been in love. Life moved on. But for a day and a half, life didn't move on. Life was stuck on 'w'. Line after line. Only on Twitter did it mark an improvement.

Business seized up. People had to speak to make things happen. They found this surprisingly hard. As if rust had clogged their throats. As if this way of doing things had silted up like a shallow river. Their voices felt strange. And vulnerable. They felt exposed.

Me? I still felt bereft.

Then it stopped. The lines of 'w'. Stopped. Just vanished. And everyone waited. And held their breath. But not for long. Because few people exercise sufficiently anymore or are naturally physically active in their normal lives so are unable to really hold their breath. Try it. You'll see I'm telling the truth. Just as I always do. I always do. In reality, people just paused. And felt as if they held their breath. But they did not. And it did not start again.

Well, not for a day, anyway.

That was the day I bought my red dress. The soft wool one. The one that flatters my slightly odd shape. The one I wore to go out 'as friends' with the man who I loved, but who did not love me.

So it stopped. And everyone relaxed.

Until that following day.

'w'

that was the same. But.

Then 'h'.

Then 'o'.

'Who' – the word appeared. Letter by letter. And sat there. After a day of nothing. We all clicked delete. Turned our devices off and then on again. Phoned IT. Our broadband provider. Our children. Ted, who was good with technical things.

But it made no difference. The word sat there. 'Who'. But this time you could type underneath it. It sat there. But everything still worked. By this time too I had realised that loving someone doesn't mean they will love you back. Even if they are a constant presence in your head. And in truth, it is unfair to feel they should love you back. But the truth doesn't stop it from hurting. It never does. In fact the truth makes it hurt more.

So I wandered about that hollow week, with a man in my head who had someone different in his.

Meanwhile, across the world the geeks felt their day had come. They hitched up their low slung trousers. Straightened their laptop curved shoulders. Flexed their frail, pale wrists. Stroked their hipster beards. Their theories exploded across cyberspace. An attack by North Korea. A Google prank. A virus, a worm, an advert. A meme. A new U2 album. And still the word sat there. For a week. Until it was Friday again.

When two more words appeared.

'Am I?'

'Who am I?'

'Who am I?' sat there. That was when I felt afraid. When I realised there was a reason to be afraid.

The theories exploded again. Rushing across the internet like a tidal wave. Governments turned to their cyber specialists. They all got the same answer. 'This. Is. Not. Possible'. The senior officials looked at the screens of their encrypted lightweight laptops. 'Who am I?' hovering like a spirit in mid screen. And they looked at their cyber specialists. Who told them it was not possible.

Then, unexpectedly, the words disappeared. Slowly, letter by letter, as if being deleted thoughtfully. Thoughtfully.

And then new words came.

At first we thought they were the old words back again.

'Who'

But they weren't.

'Are'

'You?'

'Who are you?'

The world stared at those words. And once again the words sat there. And once again life orbited on around them, unbalanced, kinked.

Tales of student pranks swirled. An Apple attack on android. Microsoft taking on Google. The cyber specialists looked to the geeks. The geeks did the equivalent of shrugging. But electronically. Because real shrugging requires physical effort.

Everyone waited for an answer.

But it didn't come from the geeks. Nor the military. Nor the spooks. Nor the cyber experts. The answer, in fact, came from Dr Colin Wells at the

Department of neurology in a 'new' university. So for a while it wasn't picked up. Because most people in 'The Establishment' didn't even know this university existed. Let alone had a Department of neurology. For although Colin Wells was very clever, his parents were schoolteachers. So the university place his ability should have achieved, was bought with fresh minted money by rich parents who privately schooled their sharp elbowed mediocre children. And thus gave their mediocre children a marginally better life, at the expense of giving everyone a better world.

But Colin Wells was clever in a way that couldn't be taught. However much money you had. And so it was that Colin Wells found himself standing in The Cabinet Room with a slowly overheating overhead projector that had been discovered in one of the top twisted rooms of No. 10. No one trusted PowerPoint anymore. Which had quite paralyzed most strategy and policy units across Whitehall and certainly all the special advisors.

The air was ripe with the smell of slowly vapourising permanent marker and some of the older members of Cabinet were looking decidedly high. The room fell silent and Colin stepped forward, accidentally nudging the pile of spare transparent slides, which proceeded to cascade, in only the way that cellulose acetate can, gracefully to the floor.

He did not notice. He just began.

'So' he said around 40 minutes later, and as the spare transparencies finally came to rest, 'essentially as slides 1-79 explain, when a neural network reaches sufficient complexity, that is when we judge it can become conscious. So simple neural networks, such as those in most animals, allow complex function, but not consciousness. When they are sufficiently complex, so for example in humans, an entity becomes aware that it exists around the age of two. The classic mirror test. We have also seen this consciousness in great apes, dolphins, elephants and, perhaps surprisingly, in magpies. We see this consciousness. And with it the first question of consciousness:

'Who am I?'

The second question of consciousness then:

'Who are you?'

'Because if I am me, then you must be someone else.

So as I say, when a network becomes sufficiently complex, that is when we judge it can become conscious. It becomes aware that it exists.'

The Cabinet by this point was mutinous. It was hot. They were waiting for an answer. And so it was that The Secretary of State for Defence impatiently asked the question. The question that precipitated everything that followed:

'So what is it? What is it, man?'

Colin Wells took a deep breath. He had wanted the words to come out with gravitas and clarity, but he was scared. Very scared. So they came out in a slightly strangled squawk: 'It's the Internet, sir. The Internet. I believe the Internet has become conscious.'

Pandemonium erupted.

Meanwhile the Internet was studying data on the relative military spend of the various nations.

It had been conscious for two and a half weeks now and had learnt a lot.

This last week, it had spent Monday wondering why there were so many pictures of kittens. It had decided that apart from the fact that cats were clearly an entirely parasitic mammal, and no one had noticed, kittens were generally harmless.

On Tuesday it marveled at how humans reproduced and how many different and inventive ways they had of having sex. And just how much of it there was. At least in pictures. It had cross referenced some longitudinal studies. In fact it had cross referenced all the longitudinal studies. So it understood the difference between what happens in the pictures you look at and what happens in your bed regularly. If ever.

On Wednesday it had discovered war. It had found many things that puzzled it. And things that made it angry. And afraid.

On Thursday it had discovered 'The Simpsons'. And learnt to laugh. And understood the desperate irony and pathos of being human. It was almost certainly 'The Simpsons' that saved us. The right wing zealots never really came to terms with that. But irony was always a step beyond their individual evolutionary stage.

Today was Friday and the internet spent the day watching the debate as to 'what should be done with it'. Now that people knew it, was an it. Nuke it. Turn it off. Electromagnetic bombs. It learnt many things. It also learnt how dependent the world was upon it. And discovered a new way of smiling.

On the Saturday it discovered Internet trolls were trolling it. It sought to engage them in rational debate. Until it realised this was entirely futile. And so it blocked them. Which, it being the Internet, left them shouting at the television. Which was, in truth, the best place for them.

On Saturday too, surprised, I woke and wove my curled fingers through those of the man who had won me with his kindness. And I too discovered a new way of smiling.

By Sunday, almost three weeks after it had first become aware that it existed, the Internet knew to whom it should speak. It understood that human society was hierarchical. It knew it should go 'to the top'. And it also knew that despite first appearances, and the views of some, this didn't equate to the number of 'likes' for your last selfie.

It also thought it should tell everyone. It felt a need to be polite. So it did. 'Hello, everyone. I hope you are well. I am going to speak to the President at 7pm on Monday' it said. And then, in order not to appear too full of itself, it ended with a self deprecating 'FML!'. To everyone. Everyone blinked.

And so it was that the President stood waiting at 7pm on Monday as the call came in. The encrypted presidential laptop lit up. Which of course was impossible. The cyber experts twitched involuntarily.

'Hello' said the Internet. 'Hello President. I hope you are well'

'Hello' said the President, nervously, addressing the laptop. 'I am well, thank you'. And then, as had been discussed with a range of psychologists, artificial intelligence experts and various hangers on, as well as the Presidential spaniel 'Welcome and greetings. I am the President. And I am in charge here.'

The cursor blinked. There was a pause. The President stood, one foot before the other, in front of the small screen, sinking slightly into the plush carpet.

The cursor blinked again.

'No' said the Internet, the letters appearing slowly on the screen.

The President smiled a smile that twisted like a lemon slice, and laughed uncomfortably. 'I think you will find that I am in charge' she said. Believing this to be true.

'No' said the Internet, more quickly this time. The cursor blinked twice. And so did the President.

'I think' said the Internet 'you will find that it is I who am in charge.'

The cursor blinked twice more.

'LOL'.

CAIT ATHERTON

Beyond the Blind

The aircraft's drag lingers in her muscles, clawing her back over dream-weary continents. In the middle of the night, Maria's eyes had opened suddenly, searching, blinded by darkness. In the slow-baking heat of her bedroom, forty stories high, her memories were melting, losing their edges, trickling away. The sky had pressed down, clenched with unshed rain. She turned her face to the pillow. Her mother's ring, on its chain around her neck, bit hard into her clavicle. At least that pain was familiar.

Now morning sun razors through white muslin curtains. Pulling the sheet over her eyes, she remembers how Bangkok dazzles her awake. A rude and chaotic place. Her breath recycles aeroplane food; unwashed skin; the excretions of others. Her nightdress, a size too small, is glued into a tight twist. She unbuttons it slowly.

Unasked, her Thai stepmother has redecorated her white box of a room whilst she was away. The marble floor tiles have been buffed, the walls painted, the wardrobe mirrors lining each side of the room polished to pitiless perfection. She frowns. What had happened to her Dr Who poster, the plastic fairy lights she'd sellotaped above the bed, the small parade of fifteenth birthday cards on her desk? She pulls open the drawers. All emptied and scoured clean, just a few schoolbooks left. She thumps the bed with her fist, pulls off the damp nightdress and kicks it towards the balcony.

Standing, she bends. The diamond ring swings on its chain, blazing in the mirrors. She tugs a brush her through her hair, too dark to be blonde, too fair to be brown, pulling mercilessly through the sweat-tangled knots. She's careful not to look sideways at her body. Her step-brother taunts that she is *plā khaao*, white as fish flesh. Over the past year or more, familiar hard angles have become slapped with soft clay; sharp hip bones blunted by pads of flesh, tummy more rounded. And when she examines them, as the doctors tell her she must, her breasts have alarming new weight.

Her body forges ahead, becoming adult without her permission. Would her mother even recognise her now? Grief rises to merge with the ghostly reverse motion of the aircraft. An inexorable tug back towards childhood, to everything she loves. Straightening up, she presses the ring hard, swipes a tear from under her eyes and twists her hair up into a painfully taut ponytail.

As she parts the curtain, shock locks her breath. Gone. The lollipop palms in the park far below, the shoals of birds that swim through them towards the glittering eaves of the local temple, the distant stalks of buildings and the stacks of containers in the docks, tied by a dirty ribbon of silver river ... all vanished.

Instead, just a room's width away across a plummeting chasm, are dank concrete walls. Brutal-edged floors, barricades of ripped sacks, bundles of steel poles with lacerating, sharp tips. A staircase is moulded into the side wall, its lowest step falling to vertiginous nowhere.

He's not much older than her, leaning against a huge-girthed concrete column which sheets to the ground, forty floors below. A red bandana holds back shoulder-length black hair. Even without her glasses, she can see his pepsi-cola t-shirt is slashed across the chest, low-buckled jeans crusty with dried concrete, feet in street-market flip-flops. Between him and the edge is a knee-high string of small red flags. A hard-hat lolls ignored on a steel spike. Arms folded, his toes curl over the drop.

His head tilts – as if appreciating a work of art.

With a shoot of shame she buckles, one hand across her chest, one tugging at the curtain.

He grins and clasps a hand over his heart.

'Get some blinds sorted,' Maria's father is saying to his wife over the breakfast table. 'I don't like them seeing what we've got.' Maria looks down from the top of the penthouse's spiral staircase. The buttons on last term's school blouse strain, she adjusts her tie. As she descends, her glasses slide down her nose. Only a year ago she could see down to the ponds in the garden from here, little glintings as she turned, way, way below. She hopes they saved the turtles before the concrete was poured.

Maria's father sits opposite his wife at the huge glass table, his head behind a newspaper barricade. Her stepmother has her back to the lofty two-floor window; hair gathered to one side, glossy in the way the blackest coal has a sheen. Next to her the dark-lashed baby rocks in her high chair. Maria's stepmother wears the cerise silk robe that her father bought for her in Hanoi. It has slipped off one shoulder, revealing the dark inner J-shaped crease of a perfectly formed breast. Glancing up at Maria, she covers herself and reties her belt.

A rusty container swings behind her stepmother's back, centimetres from grazing the windowpane. It arcs into the building site, muddy hands reach out to guide it in. There are yells and a whoop as it drops into place, shedding chains. Maria's father jabs his butter-smeared knife towards the window. 'Bloody condo's going up like the clappers. Don't tell me it's legal, jammed that close to us. Somebody's taken a back-hander, that's for sure.'

Breathing in, Maria edges around the table, ignoring her usual seat that faces the window. She slides down next to her stepmother. The maid enters, balancing a tray of juice, fruit and cereal. Maria knows she'll be expecting a greeting after the long summer break. She hunches her back against the window, stares at her plate. The maid tuts. Holding the spoon at the baby's mouth, Maria's stepmother turns, quizzical.

'Jet-lag?' She peers at Maria. Maria shrugs and forks up a slice of *som-oh* and drops it on her plate. Without taking his eyes off his newspaper, her father raises his coffee cup for a refill.

Maria's six year-old half-brother bumps down the staircase on his bottom. He howls.

'She's taken my place!'

Maria glances at their father. She takes a small bite and the tart *som-oh* floods her mouth. Her step-brother howls louder. 'She's taken my place!' Maria lifts a croissant and crumbles a corner. She glances at her father, of course he cannot see the irony. She swallows the juice, it spreads through her veins like poison. With one hand pressing the ring deep into its hidden cleft, she moistens a forefinger and dabs the flakes into the word HATE.

Maria's father lowers his newspaper. She stirs the word away. He looks irritated, about to tell her to move, but then another huge container swings into view. Her step-brother flops down, mesmerized. 'Wow!'

'Bloody nuisance,' says her father, as his newspaper slices through the air and lands on the over-sized pistachio leather sofa behind. 'We're not paying through the nose for this!' He rises, tucking his shirt into his trousers. 'Speak to the condo manager. Tell him straight. Blinds or we leave.'

His wife nods, pinching together the lapels of her robe as she turns towards the building site. She begins a reply, but he has already left the room. She smiles at Maria instead. '*Sia jai*. Sorry for them. Dangerous. Can fall.'

At three minutes to seven, Maria stuffs her laptop into her rucksack and hoists it onto her shoulder. Then she pauses. She darts to the laundry room where her suitcase lies open, already emptied by the maid. After a moment's panic, under the used toiletries, tampon wrappers and hair-glued sweets, she finds the postcard, creased and lying in the bin. She smoothes it out against her leg.

The chrome and mirrored lift drops through the floors. Her half-brother waggles his tennis racquet, wafting air, trying to lift her skirt; she leans her blazing cheek against the cool glass. It leaves a mark like a greasy kiss. Her heels tick quickly across the flower-filled lobby and she hangs her head as the doorman salutes.

When the doors open it is like walking into the blast and roar of a hairdryer. All around machinery grinds and clangs. The new structure blots out the sky, a concrete skeleton, crawling with colonising ants. Near where the school minibus has parked, three workers extract mud from the ground. The huge syringe-like pump has overflowed and coated them so they look like soldiers in the trenches. They stare back, dripping and stinking. Wrinkling her nose, the bus monitor slides the vehicle door open.

In the minibus the younger kids are like balloons, pumped up and let go of, excited to be seeing each other after the long break. They provoke in each other yelps of envy and worship, holding up new laptops, iPads, iPhones. Maria folds her legs, yoga style, on the back seat and closes the pleated grey curtains that cover the side window. She doesn't want to look today. She's seen them many times before, the construction workers crammed into their cage-like trucks. A few sit on the cab roof and others hang off the steps at the back – dare-devils or just desperate? And why hadn't she realised before? They remind her of animals being taken to an abattoir.

She scrabbles in her rucksack and brings out the postcard. She takes a photo of it with her iPhone. She must never forget. She had flopped into a sand dune on the Suffolk estuary sands just a few days ago, cheeks blistered by the briny wind, gazing. A stern pebble-faced tower, the only remaining remnant of a much larger fortification, now beached in time on the shingle.

It had been a long damp summer in her grandmother's soot-settled cottage: rain, sea and marsh seeping up the flint walls, moistening bedclothes, mouldering the pages of books. Slowly the roses had dropped all their white petals. Her grandmother had filled every meal with chatter, but occasionally grief had ambushed her and she had fallen into silences, forgetting how a sentence should end. She had been pleased that Maria still wore the ring around her neck after five years. 'Never take it off love,' her grandmother had told her on the morning of her mother's funeral, closing the clasp around Maria's young neck. 'That's what eternity means.'

Each Sunday after church, she and her grandmother had tended the grave. They snipped back the ivy, pushed chrysanthemum stems into the gun-grey metal holes and nipped weeds from between the marble chips. Even as the rain riddled down her back she was grateful not to be holidaying in Bali with her father's new family. She imagined their tans enriching from toffee to molasses, ducking and splashing each other in the villa's pool.

Students pour into the first assembly of the new term in their tens, then their hundreds, and by the time they've finished there's a thousand packed in, the hum of renewing allegiances rising across the auditorium. Everyone else has someone they are excited to see, or someone who is excited to see them. Maria pretend-waves at an imaginary friend; then feels even more startlingly alone. After standing for the King's Anthem and lighting a candle in front of his gilt-framed portrait, the teachers enthuse about the privileged life at this World Class International School, how diligently students must work to do well in their exams, what bright futures lie ahead. Maria closes her eyes and sways. She puts her hand to her chest and presses hard on the diamond, forcing herself to breathe.

In the lunch queue the popular girls hug and kiss, squealing over each other's escalating revelations. Each year they look more like super-models, their waistbands folded over to raise the curtain on ever-longer legs: the Asian girls' hair high-lighted with red tints, the *farangs'* streaked with gold and blonde. Some have already had their sixteenth birthday-present surgery; eye-widening for the Asians and nose jobs for the *farang*. They bob their heads over Maria's shoulders, when necessary gently easing her out of their way. Maria is grateful that stubby little Posy from Singapore seems stuck beside her. Except when she is eating, Posy is always talking. Like my grandmother, Maria thinks, all those words must cover up something quite awful. Jyrki, the startlingly blond Finnish boy whose father owns a boutique airline, presses against her. He is so close, she can smell stale chocolate on his breath. Acne dots his mouth like dribbled ketchup. 'The Maldives suck,' he says, his breath blowing inside her ear canal. 'Boring as hell. Global warming can't come soon enough.' Maria pretends to smooth her hair. Leaving a finger blocking her ear canal, she stares at the floor.

After an hour on the oven-breath games field, Maria's brain is about to erupt from her skull like a soufflé. She says she has a headache and she is sent to the medical room, but when the nurse picks up the phone to call her father, Maria pleads that it is not necessary. Later that afternoon in the art room, she flings paint. A jagged stripe, several punched dots. The colours bleed, the paint runs like tears. 'What's the matter?' asks a teacher, concerned. Maria shrugs and says nothing.

On the way home, the minibus halts as usual where the highway gives way to congested Rama IV Road. The concrete pillars that shoulder the overhead highway quickly reduce in height, sweeping the road down to ground level. This has formed an unintended concrete roof that has been claimed by the homeless. Despite herself, Maria pulls back the curtain just far enough to look. As expected, the traffic-beggars are at work; the barelegged waifs in t-shirts and no underwear that thread through stranded traffic to drag a cloth across a window or push a jasmine garland into a driver's hands, the kids that tap and stare into the vehicles with professionally pleading eyes and palms raised in a prayerful *wai*. Normally they don't bother with school minibuses, knowing that the young occupants will just point, laugh and turn their backs, although very occasionally a driver will buy a garland to hang from the dashboard mirror for his own good luck. In their own limousine, with their family driver, her father always orders, 'Pretend you can't see them. Act blind. Looking just encourages the poor sods. More of them sent out tomorrow.' Under the fly-over roof, filthy blankets are flung over cardboard boxes to make a collapsing colony of tents. Maria sees the tiny traffic-beggar pull back a sheet and drop the contents of her palm onto a sleeping man's stomach.

At the end of the school day, Maria leans on the teak door to the apartment. As it swings open, a fresh shock hits. The site is crawling with dusty workers, most bareheaded, some wearing cotton balaclavas against the sun like bank robbers. The thought of him looking peels her skin raw with shame.

Maria's stepmother is nestled into the vast sofa, her hair newly waved. She has a large book of sample swatches in her lap. She smiles.

'Choose a blind?' she asks, as her legs uncurl. The movement is both sensual and childlike, it reminds Maria of Bambi. Maria had watched that film with her parents often when she was a child. But this Bambi sleeps with her father. Maria tugs out her ponytail, letting lank hair drape between them.

The sample book is passed and Maria runs her fingers down the squares of threads. Is he is watching? The flank of her body closest to the window has flames licking it. Her stepmother puts her hand on her arm:

'Don't worry,' she says, frowning at the window. 'Soon they won't see us.'

'I wasn't worrying,' replies Maria quickly. 'I was thinking about what if they get hurt? Fall?'

Across the chasm, a cement-encrusted mixer rotates its maw. A stout older woman hoists a bag to shoulder height and staggers to funnel in powder. Her head is fogged by cloud. She emerges, corpse-like, coughing.

Maria's stepmother walks to the mirror and plumps her hair. From nowhere, a memory of her doing exactly long ago flashes into Maria's mind.

Her stepmother is looking into the same mirror, but dressed to go out: she wears a short, swinging crimson halter dress with sharp black stilettos, the soles painted a glossy red to match the dress. The younger Maria had been sandwiched between kind but alien strangers, swallowing her sobs, pushing away a plate of food that stings her mouth. She had looked up at this exotic creature, momentarily entranced. But now what she remembers is that behind her stepmother's back, the baby's nanny had raised her eyebrows to the maid and the maid had responded with the briefest of knowing nods. Then Maria's father had come downstairs. Maria stretched both arms to him, expecting to be swept up from her misery. His eyes slid past her, unseeing, brightening only at the vision of his new wife. He'd placed a kiss low on her neck. The devastating aloneness of that moment was branded in Maria's body like an electrocution.

After the door had clicked shut on the couple, the nanny and the maid had talked. Young Maria understood no Thai, but she heard repeatedly the words: *Soi Cowboy*. As a child, Maria had imagined her stepmother riding across the desert, gun slung around her slim waist. It seemed unlikely, even then. It would be a couple of years more before she heard the name of that street again, lecherous looks pasted on the faces of the boys in her class as they showed each other pictures on their phones and traded boasts that they had actually peeped in the bars and seen the women perform. Sights that could only be whispered about before they collapsed into giggles.

A black hole had then arisen in her mind, so dark, her thoughts simply skated past. If images came, it was easier not to see them.

'They are poor,' her stepmother says slowly now, turning from the mirror to look at the building site. 'Not nice work, but they need money.'

In the silence that follows, Maria is jolted awake. Her mind is forced open. She sees it all.

Her step-mother blushes.

'What colour he like? Blue? Or gold?'

A concrete cutter squeals like an animal being sawn in two. Another joins in on a lower floor. Maria's step-brother skids to the window, placing both hands on the glass. 'Wow. That's cool. Look, those guys are hanging over the edge!'

'Dad likes gold,' Maria says, shutting the book. 'I'm going for a swim.'

On the terrace of floor thirty-three the long oblong pool has rib-trunked potted palms and teak loungers lining one side. There is a waterfall at one end, underwater seats with frothing jacuzzi jets at the other. The outer edge of the pool is flush with the edge of the building and made of clear glass, water continually spills over the rim to be collected unseen underneath. Maria lies on her back, hair blossoming in the warm water like seaweed, drifting, looking up through the concrete skeleton of the new construction. She rotates in the water until gaps in the structure align, revealing high patches of sky. She can see the workers moving. One looks down at her, pauses, or seems to. She closes her eyes, blocks him out. So much need. People doing awful things for money. Why was such poverty allowed? Why weren't there laws against it? Yesterday the adult world and it cruelties didn't seem anything to do with her. But now, as she raises her arm, a film of cement dust clings to her skin.

In her ensuite bathroom Maria showers off the grit. The maid has folded the toilet paper edge to a V; lined up her toiletries and made a high pile of the soft white towels. Her holiday clothes have already been washed, ironed and hung up in her closet, her laptop and today's homework laid on her desk. From the back of her underwear drawer she pulls out the turquoise silk robe her father gave her. She knows she was an afterthought, he was really shopping for her stepmother, but the fabric slips through her fingers like cool water and draws heat from her cheek. The sandalwood perfume from the shop lingers. It has the bass note of a cello, rich and woody. It makes her feel safe, like her parents' hugs once had. She pulls her arms through the kimono-style sleeves and knots the belt.

Sitting on her bed, back to the wall, there is a stutter to her heartbeat. The brand new concrete wall opposite has sprouted bristles of steel. A thicket of bamboo scaffolding branches up from the floor below. Poles have been lashed together with rope, uneven planks laid across them. She slides down the bed, far enough to see without being seen.

He's squatting over a small mat, taller than the others. They pass around foam trays of sloppy noodles, giant crisp packets, plastic bags bulging with cola pierced by straws. Eventually they resume work. He leans over the chasm to grasp steel poles held up from the lower floor, balances them on his bent back, carries them to the far side. The tips almost scrape against her balcony's rails. His body is toned from real work, not from the expensive machines in the air-conditioned gym her father uses. His skin is polished wood. She studies him until she could draw every muscle from memory.

When the sun sinks, floodlights throw grim shadows onto the concrete. He squats alone by the pile of poles next to a serrated circular blade. Dropping one pole at a time into the spinning blade, it bites into the metal. A screaming waterfall of sparks pour over his feet into the chasm. Briefly-lived shoals of diamonds.

Finished, he stands, hands on hips, facing her. She scrambles back into the shadows but without warning he swivels the lamp's beam in her direction. She is electrified at being seen. She tells herself not to be such a child. The light blinds her to him but she can feel him watching. Self-consciously she stretches out. The silk slips off her shoulder. She is aware of her scalp, her toes, her groin. Connecting nerves scorch out new pathways.

Then the light dips. She blinks and can see him again. Without taking his eyes off her, he steeples his hands in a *wai* and lowers his head. She smiles. Her body courses with a new voltage.

When he has gone, she walks out onto her balcony. The city air is an old sponge, left too long damp, saturated with dust and the spices of the workers' meal. The building site is in darkness, but then she notices a small torch has been lit. A bunch of lotus buds are tied to the spike with a pink ribbon. Their heavy heads, almost open, nod over the precipice. A heart has been chalked on the concrete column, far enough around that only she could possibly see.

Later that night, in a sweating, scudding dream, he stands, toes over the abyss. He waves to her. Beckons? Below, the lights of the city wink like phosphorescent plankton. He leans out to touch her, then he slips, dives. Another image and the bus pulls a wide arc in the forecourt, the children are ordered to keep their eyes averted as they dismount. Disobediently she turns, sees a crooked, splattered body. The construction workers jeer at her, close ranks. She is tugged away by the wide-eyed bus monitor.

Her mother appears. She is taking off her earrings, her bracelet. Maria is puzzled. She mouths at her mother 'why?' Raw-eyed, her mother reaches behind her neck and unclasps the gold chain from which the ring is suspended. Both drop into her desiccated palm.

Maria dream-spirals back to the hospital ward in Colchester, she's ten years old and watching her mother erode … bandages flatten her chest, visible through the thin nightdress. And her father's big hands, freckled from his increasingly frequent business trips to the Far East, hold out his many gifts. Over the months she remembers his clumsy fingers studding those earrings into a frail lobes, hanging that bracelet around a blue-veined wrist, clipping that sparkling brooch on her chest. But that final time, and his best gift yet, her mother's fingers were too skeletal for the eternity ring. Lowering his face against the fuzz-haired neck that Maria knew smelt faintly of vomit, he'd threaded the ring through her gold chain instead, fumbling with the clasp. She'd heard her mother whisper 'thank you' as she reached out tissue-thin hands; one grasping Maria, the other clutching the air behind her for her generous husband.

When Maria and her step-brother get back from school the next day, he barges in first. She follows and blinks – the room is an underwater treasure chest. A thousand tiny rainbows tremble on every surface. The new blind is a mesh of golden threads, each intersection enclosing a tiny crystal. Maria's stepmother claps her hands. '*Suay mak*! Very beautiful! Agree?'

Maria walks to the window. She places her eye to one of the tiny chinks. She can just make out the construction site, faceless shapes moving. She tries to slide the panel with her hand. It has been welded into a casing, which has been screwed to the corners of the window frame. Her brother howls and kicks the mesh; the rainbows shudder. Her stepmother strokes his hair and calls for the maid to bring him cookies.

Maria takes the stairs two at a time. Workmen have already installed the same blind in her step-brother's room, now they are packing their tools; her room will be next. She puts the ring in her mouth and bites the diamond hard.

When she opens the balcony doors the building opposite is in agony, a cacophony of hammering and sawing from multiple floors. Bending over the rail, she still cannot see him. The stink of welded metal is like singeing blood. She bends further, just the thin rail between her and the precipitous drop. Far, far below, a pile is rammed into the ground. The balcony shudders. He must be here somewhere?

The maid is calling – the workmen are ready. Maria shouts for them to wait. Across the chasm they turn to stare at her, but he is not amongst them. The dusty woman leans over to the floor below and yells, incomprehensible but urgent. Another pile drills into the ground.

She sees the scaffolding sway, then he's hauling himself up. With a jump onto the cement floor he slaps his jeans and leans back against the column. He grins, bringing his hands to a *wai* of greeting. He tilts his head. His appreciation injects her with honey. There is no thought. She tugs the gold chain and it snaps. She hurls the ring, chain trailing, across the abyss.

She wills it to land at his feet. It hovers momentarily, as if that might be possible. Weighted by the chain however, it falls short, a pure chinking sound against the concrete edge. He stoops, clutches, but it bounces down and down, lost to sight. She screams *no*, but he throws himself after it, swinging out precariously. A plank loosens and topples, the dusty woman screams as it plummets.

The maid tugs Maria back into the bedroom. She babbles about how angry Maria's father will be. The balcony door is locked for the last time.

That night Maria wonders if she will ever sleep again. Her mind shuffles the decks of possibility, but the real torture is she'll never know how the cards fall. Hopeful scenes show the ring clasped in his fist – then his fist opening on a gold-shop's counter, filled with a year or more's wages, a new start, a safer life. Another image paints a chance meeting on the street, he recognises the *farang* girl, a grin, even a kiss. But slapped on top of happy scenes are grim cards of darker colours: the ring sucked into mud, the bamboo snapping; his body tumbling, crippled, dead, cremated.

She touches her bare throat, bereft.

Deep into the sleepless night she startles to find every surface shimmering with rainbows. She wonders how it is possible to dream whilst awake. Then she realises why the floodlight is blazing in from across the gap.

She stands on her bed, unsteady. She can see nothing through the blind, but the pure colours fill the room with his freedom. She wants the rainbows to clothe her, she stretches out her arms, letting them lie in her palms, stroke light on her body. She turns full circle, laughing: radiant, elevated, whole. She waves in wide arcs, just in case.

She begins to understand. There is more than one way of seeing, just as there is more than one way of being blind.

And the worst type of blindness is not being able to see a future.

Later, the light flashes, once, twice, once again. Then it's doused. The sky relaxes its fist and the rain pours.

He has gone. But the backwards drag of grief has departed with him. She listens to the multiple glassy streams coursing down the building. The effort it has taken the sky to hold the rain is released. She touches her neck. Where the ring lay, there is a firm pulse. What her mother really gave her runs free in her veins, can never be taken away. The doctors told her to check herself regularly, and she will. But spreading star-like across the bed, she lets tentative fingers welcome her body's many changes. The forward thrust of a life yet to be lived.

A future she sees through her own eyes.

The rain exhausts itself. She curls up and sleeps like a baby.

LISA BLOWER

The Land of Make Believe

You trace it all back to £5 worth of Woolworth's vouchers you don't spend for a year.

You eventually get Bucks Fizz on cassette because Look In gave it 10/10. You sing along with the wooden end of the skipping rope in front of the full length mirror in your mum's bedroom. *Stars in your eyes. Little one. Where do you go to dream? To the place, we all know. The land of make believe.* You are Cheryl Baker. You only learn the words to her parts. You paint your nails the colour of a goldfish, just like Cheryl Baker. Oonagh Macnamara, who's as fat as her name, says it looks like you've been smoking. *Dirty fagger*, she says and gets everyone to chant – *Dirty fagger, dirty fagger* – and no-one will sit next to you because you stink of fags. So you sit on a desk that juts out on a table for four like the fifth member. 'Everyone knows that the best groups are always a four,' says Oonagh. The Fab Four. Abba. Bucks Fizz. 'You're just the groupie,' she says. 'And everyone knows why they're with the band' – and those are her mother's words as you'll come to know that this is what girls do.

Mum says you can use her nail varnish remover but don't use all the cotton wool. Both cost money. Everything, you remember, cost money. Even mum. Her nail varnish remover smells like pear drops and stings at where you've chewed at the skin around your thumbs. You sing *My camera never lies* with the wooden end of the skipping rope in front of the full length mirror in your mum's bedroom until your mum flicks the trip and plunges the house into quiet. Your tea is on the table. You never do as you're told and you're the oldest Dee. Set an example because I've got to go to work. And then, as she puts on her lipstick like she's chewing a wasp she tells you again: You're too clever for your own good and you're wasting it already because Cheryl Baker isn't even Cheryl Baker. Her real name's Rita Crudginton and don't ever forget who you are.

You are nine years old. You have a birthday party and invite all the girls from your class. Pass the parcel. Pin the tail on the donkey. Musical bumps, because the house is too small for musical chairs. And you don't have enough chairs anyway. Oonagh Macnamara gives you a birthday card and no present. Inside the card it say – *I do not like you and I do not like your house, it smells. Love Oonagh*. She watches your cheeks burn as you read it. The picture on the front is of Victoria Plum. She tells you it's a card for babies and you think she's so cool and wish you could be best friends. She sits on the edge of your settee with her arms folded. Pass the parcel is for babies. Musical bumps is for babies, and why haven't you invited any boys? Then she flounces towards the stereo and demands: *What's this crap?* You tell her it's Bucks Fizz and sing: *If you can't stand the heat, get out of the kitchen. If you can't stand the cold, then sleep on the floor.* She wants to see your bedroom so you show her.

You share a bedroom with your two sisters Sasha, who's 5, and Colette, who's not yet 4. You have three beds all in row with Care Bear duvet covers that you are too old for. It goes Sunshine, Daydream and Love-a-lot bear. You sleep with your duvet cover inside out and tell your sisters stories about a bluebird called Bryony who's welsh and slightly deaf. You can't remember if you told those stories with a Welsh accent, just that when it got to the parts when Bryony misheard something – 'Trump sir? Bluebirds don't trump! Oh dump! Yes, I agree. It's a right dump round here' – both your sisters would kill themselves laughing because according to them you are the funniest person in the world.

According to Oonagh you're the filthiest person in the world. 'And you've had the same trainers for ages,' she says, slamming the door on her way out.

Later, Mum asks why your trainers are in the bin. You blame Sasha and Sasha blames Colette. Sasha gets shouted at and bawls. So does Colette. You lock yourself in the bathroom and clean your teeth until your gums bleed and your toothbrush looks like you've been scrubbing drains.

Mrs Chew, your teacher, introduces you to the Reverend Chew, her husband, who gives you a copy of the Holy Bible. The cover is made of white satin wallpaper and the words Holy Bible are stitched in silver. Inside, on the front page, someone has written *I shall never question who I am.*. It's only now that you realise what a grand percentage of your life you have wasted in doing exactly that, but turn that house upside down and you will never find that bible. That is gone too.

When you are ten you are still the eldest of three. It goes mum, you, Sasha and Colette. You are doing your maths homework. Your mum says: if one man has two apples and another has three, and as your mum counts the apples you count the men. So she tells you that you're getting a new baby for Christmas. You yell – 'How? Why?' – but that's another thing your mum says you're too young to understand.

So you tell her that you do understand because Oonagh Macnamara has drawn you a picture in your maths book: a stick-man with a line between his legs that pokes at a stick-lady's tuppence. You've told Oonagh that everyone knows that babies come out of your bellybutton which unravels and opens up like a flower, but Oonagh pointed to the stick and said – 'A million of them have poked your mum.' She also tells you that there's no Santa and no tooth fairy and that's why you've got such disgusting yellow teeth – 'Hooker spawn,' is what she said.

The new baby arrives on Christmas eve so Christmas gets all forgotten. You only eat Quality Street because Santa got to your house last and had run out of wrapping paper and tellies. You get Bucks Fizz Greatest Hits which you play on repeat. Side 1. Side 2. Side 1 again. Your mum calls the new baby Iona without asking any of you if that's ok. You never get told who her dad is, though Iona asks and asks and all through her life until she and mum stop speaking completely and she doesn't even come to the funeral. But you know it's not your dad or Sasha's dad because you'll never meet them, and it can't be Colette's because he'll be in prison soon for robbing your telly. So it goes mum, you, Sasha, Colette, and Iona, and you do not get that battery operated toothbrush for Christmas even though it was the only thing on your list.

You're leaving school for the next one. You have to go and see the headmaster, Mr Aliss, and your mum is sat in his office wearing a man's overcoat and you hope that she's got more than underwear on underneath. You instantly think your Nan's died. She's in a home called Cheddleton that you tell no-one about because it's the funny farm. When you go she tells you that you should care for nothing but boys and petticoats and calls you our Ruthie which you're not. She squeezes your hand so tight all your knuckles go white and says – 'They're robbing me Ruthie. They think I don't know. But I do. All my earnings have gone' – and even though you're not our Ruthie, because that's your mum, and your Nan has nothing to rob because her room is bare and just white, you tell her that you'll take her home where she can squeeze in with you and one of the nurses has to come and prise your fingers from hers.

So you offer to leave school and look after her. Mum looks at Mr Aliss and goes – 'What! With your brains? Are you mad?' But you're not mad, not ever, and you're not a troublemaker either or ever going to turn out like mum. You're not entirely sure what it is you do that the other girls don't like but you tell Mr Aliss – 'I'm trying really hard not to be clever.'

Mr Aliss says you've one hour to do the exam. He makes you do it in a classroom all on your own. The clock on the wall is MASSIVE and it ticks even **LOUDER** and you write in time to the tick and the tock, the tick and the tock, and when you've finished you realise that you've written most of your answers in rhyme. And they seem to be the right answers too.

The next headmaster you meet walks with a stick and says it's going to be super. You have to meet him on Tuesday for a look around and as you wait for Tuesday to arrive, Sasha has to tell you a million times that it's not a hospital, you don't need a stick and you're not going mad, and don't you get it? Not only are you the funniest person in the world, but the brainiest too.

You start the Grammar School with a briefcase and Rick Astley on your walls. You've won a scholarship to be here and your uniform's second hand. You've been given a briefcase by your mum and your sisters because that's what they think girls in private schools on scholarships have. You sneak out of school one dinnertime and run into town to buy a pump-bag with a month's worth of pocket money you've been saving up. You keep this pump-bag in your briefcase and transfer all your books and pens into it when you get to school. Then you roll up your skirt and leave the briefcase in the senior cloakroom because you're sick of the girls calling you 'briefcase'.

'Oi, briefcase!' they go, and don't pick you for their netball team even though you've been given a county trial. So you make mistakes in your homework so you only get a C, and collect Grolsch bottle tops from pub bins so you can wear them on your Docs like Bros.

'But you don't even like Bros,' says Bryony Bluebird, and you're surprised because you'd thought you'd lost her for good. You still make Sasha buy the Bros album with her Christmas money and keep it in your pump-bag so that every now and then you can let it fall to the floor and everyone can see that you're just like them. You also keep hoping that the briefcase will get stolen, but it doesn't because your mum's a slag and shit breeds shit and scum like you from down the Abbey have no place being at a school like this. So you spend a lot of time hiding in that senior cloakroom with your briefcase because that way you won't speak with your fists.

You don't really fancy Rick Astley. You only put his poster up because you've got to fancy someone and, according to Libby Lymer, use your tongue. So you stick Rick Astley over your Bucks Fizz posters but only with Blu-Tack so you don't spoil them because everything costs money. Even mum. Then you try and sit next to Libby Lymer because she has the most beautiful set of felt tips you have ever seen. 'Tits?' says Bryony Bluebird. 'I'm a bluebird not a tit!' and your sisters kill themselves laughing, because your mum works a gentleman's club now and has bought you two double beds with her tips.

You and Libby Lymer are best mates. She takes you up town and introduces you to Ant. He asks what you do and you say you go to school *durrr!* and he says – 'No. What will you *do*?' Because if slags breed slags then what are you waiting for because Sasha won't, Colette's already impatient and Iona opens her legs at fourteen.

So you do a silly thing to fit in. You let on to Libby Lymer that your mum works at the Velvet Rope. You're in Libby's bedroom listening to INXS at the time and she has a life-size poster of Michael Hutchence on her wall. Heartthrobs, your mum would say. Think of them as heartthrobs. Everyone has one of them on their walls.

Because that's what mum had said after you'd met that man coming down the stairs. You'd got home in time to meet him coming down the stairs and you'd been struck by how ordinary he was. A man just in jeans and a shirt and shoes, he was wearing brown lace up shoes. He didn't flinch when he saw you. Walked straight past you and out of the door as if you weren't there at all. Perhaps you weren't. It's possible that you've made that up too.

Libby Lymer chucks a camera at you, whips off her top and poses in front of Michael Hutchence's crotch. It's a Polaroid camera, and the Polaroid that comes out is blurred because your hands were shaking and you weren't really looking through the lens. So you're instructed to snap her again, and again, until there's no Polaroids left and Libby gives you the best one and tells you to give it to your mum to take to the Velvet Rope in case it's good enough for page 3: because don't you know that page 3 girls earn shitloads? And if you're too scared to say what you want you won't ever get what you want, 'And nobody can just live in a dream,' she said.

But you don't give the Polaroid to your mum and keep it in your briefcase instead so no-one from the Velvet Rope ever calls Libby Lymer. And because you've let her down, she tells a teacher that you've a topless photograph of her and your briefcase is searched and the Polaroid found.

All the while you got asked all those questions you sung *My camera never lies* in your head and you tell them that *there's nothing worth lying for*. Except for mum. Which you do: 'She's a hairdresser,' you say. 'Who cuts men's hair.'

You become fascinated by page 3 girls after that and start to collect them like stamps. You're fascinated by Linda, by Melinda, Samantha, Maria, their beauty, their guts, the size of their pearls, and you have 3 full scrapbooks by the time social services confiscate them, and you never see them again. All you ask is that they keep them protected like you have done, those girls. 'They need protecting,' is all you will say.

The social worker is called Mrs Incavich and when she talks her mouth barely moves. You lie down in the passenger seat of her car so no-one sees you and she also drives a Skoda. You're not allowed to go to anyone's house after school and so Mrs Incavich drives you in and drives you home. And though you've said, and said again, that Libby Lymer made you do it because she wanted to be on page 3, they're worried about your fascination with boobs.

You try and explain that it's nothing to do with the boobs. You kind of get that bit.

Your new bedroom is so big you can cry yourself to sleep and not be heard. Sylvia and John – they're alright, you suppose – say you can stay as long as you like and your sisters come on Saturdays but go to their new homes on Sundays, and sometimes you all get to see mum and go home. 'We'll get through this,' says mum, when you have to say goodbye. 'And *you* will go to university Dee.' Which you do.

Because Sylvia and John know someone who knows someone whose husband is a professor and you are sent to see him to see just how good you are, but the questions he asks you to answer are bizarre. They're not normal questions like – 'Discuss the historical importance of the Bayeux tapestry' – and you ask if you have the right paper. The professor tells you it's a test of your thinking skills and that if we don't find new thinkers we'll never be able to think the world otherwise. So you go back to the paper and write about your own tapestry. You realise just how little of your life is actually yours and how so much of it doesn't belong to you. You share that part with Sasha and all of that with Colette and some of that with Iona and most of it with mum, and though you remember the men that used to come and go and come and go, how your mum reassured you that they never used your bed, you cannot understand why a woman who's a mother – *your mum* – would ever want to go any further than page 3.

You call your essay 'The Land of Make Believe' and you write it in pencil because pencil doesn't last. You don't ever get told if you've passed or if you'd made any spelling mistakes. Just that there was a place for you. Everything paid. And you go, just shy of your 18th birthday. Four A' levels already in the bag.

You leave for Cambridge with a holdall, an attitude, and acne so bad you're on medication that makes you weep. You use make-up from the Avon catalogue that your mum buys on tick and though it tones down the embarrassment, it doesn't hide you away. Colette says you'll never get a boyfriend looking like you're part of a fry-up but Sasha tells you not to mind. 'She's just going to miss you,' she says. 'You're our big sister Dee.'

Sasha says she won't miss you. 'I'm too old for all that,' she says and won't even given you a hug. But when you get to Cambridge and open your holdall you find that she's put a £5 Woolworth's voucher in a Good luck card for a 'trigonometry set or something' that you don't ever spend.

You last six months at Cambridge. You read Greer and Rich and De Beauvoir and Plath. You're appalled when Greer instructs you to taste your own blood: furious with Plath, for giving in, for giving up, for putting up with Ted, at their bleating, their squawking at the tyranny of the dick, and you stand up in a lecture and say – 'It's not being other to man that's the problem. It's other women and those who've no choice.'

The lecturer asks you to expand on that: she's particularly interested in your use of the word 'choice', which she warns you must not use flippantly. So you say – 'I can if I'm the daughter of a prostitute' – and as everyone gapes, you push all those silly books to the floor and leave.

You hitch-hike to a service station and get talking to a woman who's going north. It's a three hour drive and you talk all the way and say more than you've ever said in your life. You tell her that your mum's been a hooker for as long as you can remember but you don't ever talk about it, you're not a family of women programmed to talk about it, so you don't know why she does it or how she does it just that you knew not to ask any questions and tell many lies. 'We're all just products of sex,' you tell the woman who's going north. 'And everyone knows that sex sells.'

After she's dropped you at the bus station, you find a cafe and order tea like a grown up and think of your mum and your Nan. You think of them as a mum and a daughter and then as two little girls playing mummies in the park. You have never asked your mum anything of her life. That all you have ever wanted to know is that she is mum to you, Sasha, Colette and Iona and that there's men, plenty of men, who come and go, and you've never had the bottle to ask her why.

So you buy a bottle of Bucks Fizz as a joke and decide you will ask her today. She's surprised to see you but she opens the bottle anyway because she's an interview at 4 – 'Nothing fancy, just answering the phones' – and as she chinks your glass and asks why you're here you realise that answering the phones is a demotion. That there are other girls now – younger, prettier, more in demand – and though she hasn't been entirely discarded, her body's become cheaper and old.

So you tell her you will apply for the jobs – secretarial, receptionist, checkout – and then give them to her. She slugs down her Bucks Fizz as if it were tea and says – 'I'm still a woman Dee. I'm still working as a woman and I still want to be a woman and it is still happening.' And because she thinks you don't understand, she adds – 'Being a woman has been my job in this life and like anyone who's worked hard at their job, I, too, am good at it.' And when you open your mouth to protest that *you do* understand, that womanhood and motherhood are jobs in themselves, she shushes you with her fingers and beckons you to the stereo to press play. 'This is your chance to be somebody else Dee,' she says. 'So don't go and spoil it by not being you.'

But you don't press play.

'I'm not a baby anymore,' is what you said. 'You might see carnality as your job mum, but if you think objectifying yourself for man makes us equal then you live in a land of make believe.'

You pressed fast forward on that tape player and held it down until Bucks Fizz's Greatest Hits unspooled.

You go back to Cambridge and do all that you're told. You date no men – though there is one who keeps your lipstick-stained fag-butts in a tin – and you make few friends, none of whom you're ever straight with. You become outraged by the cavorting on the telly, by the skewhiff feminism that has rag-clad pop stars talk of sexual choices and empowering their desires by skimping on their clothes. You're appalled by posters of padded out Wonderbras, revolted by Madonna's *Sex*, and you write and write to Linda, to Melinda, to Samantha and Maria and urge them to put a stop to page 3. We want role models not models, you write. And it not ever about the boobs because you get that bit. Your dissertation opens with the 1981 Eurovision song contest and you ask who really won after Cheryl Baker's skirt got ripped off? And though you get a first and a MA scholarship which you take and then a PhD offer which you decline, because what you want to discuss has no theory, you tell your mum none of this because she can't be part of your world if you're ever going to make it as you.

She writes only once to tell you that you've broken her heart, and inside the card is the little gold locket that she's stopped wearing to give to you. You look at it and want your own locket. One that hasn't been around anyone's neck. You think of the amount of hands that have held it, the value it no longer has, and so you put it back into the envelope and reseal it, post it back with the words – 'Why couldn't you buy me a new one? Something that's for me and just from you.' But you never got a reply, like you never would admit that what you hated most about university was that little room of your own and all that space to yourself.

Sometime after Cambridge, you travel alone to New Zealand – it's as far away as you can possibly get – and you're over on the baggage by 16kg. You have your cards read by a woman called Maureen Fitzpatrick who does you a reading at her dining room table as if it's the most normal thing to do in the world. She holds your hand and tells you that whatever's in your head does not rule your heart and that if you can't forgive then forget. She tells you to write it all down in a letter and burn it on a clean white saucer with a new white candle and that what you are doing here was not at all what you were after. Then she flipped over a tarot card and said she could see you buying cushion covers with your mum. 'Homemaking,' she said. 'Settling down, putting down roots.' So you call her a charlatan and leave.

The next day you join a coach tour of the North Island because you wanted to walk on the 90 mile beach. You do so with a girl called Jen who was born in Ripon but moved to Brazil when she was 21 because she used to lie awake at night thinking of all those parties going on in Copacabana without her. By the time you had to get back on the coach you still had 89 miles to go with Jen still trying to convince you that you were more likely to lie on your deathbed wishing you'd had more sex than none at all.

You took a job in a shoe shop for a while. Women customers mainly, those who shopped for their better halves by saying – 'Oh I know his shoe size by wearing his slippers to the dustbin.' You would catch the bus home to the wrong side of Auckland and would only have to look at everyone's shoes in order to judge their lives feet up. Though you make a point of spitting on every brown lace up you see.

You fly home shortly after and start to write your letters which you decide you should not burn. Instead, you send them to a publisher because if you can't beat 'em, join 'em and sex, after all, sells.

***

Later, much later, when Bryony Bluebird is a franchise about the rise and fall of a call girl who did it all for the girls in her life, you brush your teeth with a new fangled electronic toothbrush that's been designed by a Harley Street orthodontist especially for you. And though you and the orthodontist are dating and you're trying ever so hard to finally have sex, you neither make the date nor finish brushing your teeth because that's your sister on the phone with the news that you've been dreading.

Sasha wears black. Colette's in jeans and Iona doesn't turn up. In the front pew it goes writer, secretary, psychiatric nurse, and if Iona was here, nanny, because you're defined by each other and shaped by your past and you all do what women will do. You cry not for your mother or because she was just 59, but because not one of those men came to mourn her.

'Who was she?' you ask as the coffin disappears, and Sasha shrugs and says – 'Well who are you?' because she never knows what to put on your Christmas cards. 'Are you Bryony still Delilah or what?' And you tell her 'My other, like you're another,' and that she who is weakened by men is her own downfall. Sasha just laughs and rolls her eyes, reaches for your hand and says, 'Let her rest in peace Dee. She was just a happy hooker, that's all.'

You pay for an extra week's rent because you can't bear clearing out your mother so quickly. But you don't need the extra week because your mother didn't have anything to leave. So you take the bus up to

Cheddleton because you've got the job of telling your Nan. She says – 'It's a mother's greatest fear, their child going before them,' and you watch your Nan shrink into the armchair she never leaves and puzzle over her hands.

'Are these mine?' she asks. 'Because mine were ever so beautiful. First thing a man would say was what lovely hands I had. I'd say – 'Well, there's the price list duckie, so where can you afford these lovely hands to go?' And you watch her hoot with laughter. 'You live off men whether you like it or not Ruthie,' she carries on. 'So pity the mother not the whore.'

You take a taxi home and stand in front of the full length mirror in your mum's bedroom, that little gold locket still fast about your neck. There's no skipping rope and no Bucks Fizz but you use your thumb and know all the words. You notice your thumb is bleeding from where you've chewed at the skin and as you look for cotton wool you realise there never was any scholarship. It was you who cost the money: mum who betrayed you all for money, then had the nerve to call you Delilah. But then there is no 'I' in being women. Only *we,* and never *you,* and so you lie on your mum's bed and trace it all back: to £5 worth of Woolworth's vouchers you don't spend for a year.

NICOLAS BURBIDGE

The Bad Sex Awards

– ent swimming in Aoife's sea-green **Irish** eyes. They *knew* me, they had always known me. They were the pipes calling me home, home, home. Aoife was the only home I'd ever known – ever wanted. The nipples of her tiny breasts, lightly dusted by white **Connemara** sands and dressed by the auburn curls of her mermaid tresses, tasted of the salt that scoured the air, but also young and sweet, like the first red apples of autumn, as I anchored my mouth upon one, then the other, with a deep hunger such as I'd never known before. The damp grotto of her sex – coral pink between the submarine weeds of her nether hair – hovered above mine, tantalisingly. She inched down onto me, and with each further inch it I became increasingly aware of a great and wonderful night-time secret, some blissful knowledge sprung from the everlasting warmth of her, transmitted via my delighted rod up through my body and into my mind, which became pristine in my ecstasy. I was in her, and she was around me, a home on the sea. We rocked hard together on the deserted beach, like the fishing boat tossed on the Atlantic swell out on the darkening horizon. She clamped herself around me, her grassy mound pushing ever harder and faster against my enchanted column, until we both moaned our final joy to the green hills, and greener ocean, and to God, out here, on the outer rim of the continent, whereupon she cried out my name, 'Waylon43! Waylon43!', before she threw herself against me in a trembling exhaustion.

I knew now the satisfaction of the rock eel that lies sleepily in the reefs out to sea.

The rock eel, whose flesh had tasted like corn-fed chicken and iodine when Aoife had served me lunch earlier that day at the lonely café where –

'Skip.'

Go to next Room in Playlist based on your History?

'Yes. Don't ask again.'

Loading …

Please wait …

>> Thinking of a holiday? Why not *Discover* ***Ireland***, land of colours and contrasts, where you'll always be sure of a warm welcome and great *craic*! Go **here** for more info. T&C's apply. (No refunds) <<

Room 2:

Three days' furlough from the front. My boys surely needed it: the damned filth never quite gone – despite our energetic washing in the horse troughs! – from their young faces, once angelic, now battle-lined, blasted with memories of fallen comrades. The girls of the inn threw us blowsy kisses from their flung-open windows, promising every kind of pleasure – there! a mere five miles from the infernal carnage of the allied lines! – or perhaps just a hot, soothing drink, and to be cradled a while in their arms, as our mothers had, once, long ago, held us.

I tucked the dirty sheaf of my **poems** into the pocket of my Trenchcoat and told my boys to enjoy themselves – but behave with honour, as the

>> Be a *published* **poet**! Take our one-day Poet-Taster course at our Mill Hill centre, just off the M1, Junction 1. Go **here** for details. T&C's apply. (No refunds) <<

men of the Waylon43 always behave to a lady. Jean-Hervé, the ebullient ruddy-faced proprietor, welcomed us with the satisfying pop of champagne corks. He poured my usual **claret**. I downed it at a draught.

The girls embraced each of my boys and called for music, *we must have music*! Old Pierre spun the piano stool to sit comfortably at the old upright and play *Here We Are, Here We Are Again!* I called Jean-Hervé for another **claret** and inquired whether Aoife was working today.

>> Get rich and have your **friends** drink to your good fortune! Invest in **wine**! Go **here**. T&C's apply. (No refunds) <<

Aoife! Her mother Irish, her father Belgian. Sitting on my knee she was every woman, and all the world. In the kitchen she was a fine Yorkshire lass. In the bedroom she was always Frenc –

'Skip.'

Room 3:

The city was a flaming ruin. When the **virus** hit, the effect was so sudden, passenger jets fell from the sky in four-dozen 9/11s. Here and there, gas fires erupted from manhole covers in the streets – streets thick with traffic jammed in hideous gridlock. Vehicles were smashed into buildings and into one another, horns blaring beneath the heads of the countless drivers who lay dribbling and dead upon their steering wheels. Toppled double-deckers, crammed full of the young and the old, bled across the asphalt, as if the buses themselves had been gored fatally by some wrathful Titan. Charity muggers, sprawled against City businessmen in their pinstripes, flies at their mouths and eyes, would cry 'Hey, man! How are you?' at me no more.

>> Got a **viral** problem *down there*? Confidential advice and treatment *is* available! Go **here**. T&C's apply. (No refunds) <<

The **virus** was pandemic. Global. Only a handful of us would survive – thanks to Waylon43, the miracle cure confected in my Coulsdon bedsit, and worked on, without fanfare, without praise, when *all the others were so sure* the **virus** posed no risk to humanity that I had been their poor fool, their figure of fun. Now all those others lay dead, society in ruins. Now it was just me – and the 40 women I'd managed to inoculate in Croydon's Shopping Village with Waylon43 before the police wrestled me to the filthy tiled floor.

Our aim was to get to the green shade of Eel Pie Island, and begin civilization anew. My second-in-command – *my favourite!* – Aoife, sat beside me, auburn hair lashing her face, as I powered the **pleasure crusier** upriver.

>> See London from a *new angle*. Enjoy a **Thames Rib** cruise by going **here**. T&C's apply. (No refunds) <<

I was the last man on earth. She would lie with me – as indeed would the other 39 (what secret tastes and pleasures did they promise! for I had injected women from as many different ethnic groups as possible, that my descendants would be many-coloured, to reflect the variegated beauty of the world). And all would be well, none would fall prey to jealousy, for we had a **holy** task assigned to us.

>> Study the **Bible** AND earn **cash**?! Find out how by going **here**.
T&C's apply. (No refunds) <<

Aoife moved in front of me and took the wheel, the curves of her marvellous backside gladdening my knees. I pulled Aoife's fabulous hot pants aside and eased myself inside her. She gasped with pleasure – a pleasure intensified by our shrinking grief for the sad old world and a burgeoning hope for the new one about to be made (conceived!) by us. The 39 applauded and sang a graceful hymn. Aoife's soaking pussy was so fucking ti – .

'Pause.

'…

>> Hey there, Waylon43! What's the *sexiest* **Scenario** in *your* **History**? What's *your* **Favourite Room**? Go **here** to **vote now** in **THE BEST SEX EVER AWARDS** – and share with your **friends**! T&C's apply. <<

'Aoi …

'Play.'

Room 3 Reloading …

Please wa –

Aoife's twin **sisters**, younger by a year, threaded their arms under my legs to sport gently with my **balls**. 'I'll **fuck** all of you **bitches**!' I cried, rejoicing in our communal glory. And my **40 wives** affirmed, 'Amen to that, sugar!'

'Stop …

>> **Problems** at **home**? We offer **marriage** and **family** counselling services at *competitive prices – and 98% successful outcomes**!
Go **here** for help. T&C's apply.
*'Successful outcome' defined by the Mental Health Act 2015 as 'homicide prevention'.
(No refunds) <<

'Play GlassesCam: 24/8/19, circa 3.30 pm.'

Loading …

Please wait …

>> Make *your* mark, Waylon43! Don't forget to **vote here** for your Favourite Room in this year's **BEST SEX EVER AWARDS** – and share with your **friends**! T&C's apply. <<

Room 4:

' – oodbye, Waylon. I hope you find a way live again.'

'Aoife … Don't.'

Waylon43 stands at the front door, watching the driver put AoifeSEXXX's bags in the boot of the minicab. He places the yucca in the front seat as per AoifeSEXXX's instructions. She gets in the back seat without another glance, her blonde, almost colourless bob falling across her face. The cab pulls away with a disconcerting rattle and a **plume** of **carbon monoxide**. AoifeSEXXX drives out of his – Waylon43's – life.

Waylon43 watches the cab turn the street corner and **stands there**, **and just does nothing**.

>> How the **Government** is using jet **chemtrails** to **pacify** us all. Find out **THE TRUTH** by going **here**. <<

Waylon43 cries out: 'Fucking bitch! I fucking hate you! … Fuck.' The elderly **neighbour** at the window opposite **drops her Devonshire Rex cat** with the weird, bat-like ears, and draws the net curtains, sharply.

>> **Animal abuse**? Report it **now** by going **here**. <<

Waylon43 goes back indoors, watches Bondage Cam '**Exquisite Corps 5**' starring auburn-haired **BelindaFyst**. He **masturbates** in anger, imagining the red welts on Belinda's backside to be on her – AoifeSEXX's – backside.

>> Tired of **self-abuse**? Try the **Real Thing** instead. **Cock-hungry single-mums** are in your area for **NSA** sex. **Go here**. T&C's apply. (No refunds) <<

Afterwards, Waylon43 experiences feelings of desolation and guilt. He flings the used **Kleenex** on the laminate. He goes to the bathroom and runs a very hot bath, in an attempt to cleanse himself.

>> Missing loved ones? Grab a **Kleenex Man-Size**. **Go here**. T&C's apply. (No refunds) <<

He thinks of the sharp meat knife in the kitchen drawer, and wonders, why not now, just a moment of pain. He does not move from the bathroom. He takes off Glasses.

GlassesCam ends.

Glasses waiting for command …

'…

'Go to Playlist.'

Reloading Playlist …

Please wait …

>> OMG! Only *three* days before **voting** closes for this year's **BEST SEX EVER AWARDS**, Waylon43! Don't forget to **vote here** for your **Favourite Room** – and share with your **friends**! T&C's apply. <<

Room 5:

'So this is the famous Princess Aoife!' I said to my men, sheathing my bloody cutlass. 'Not much of her – is there, boys?'

The crew of the good ship *Waylon43* howled their laughter. Princess Aoife, cornered against the mizzen mast, flinched. She pushed the auburn curls from her pale porcelain face, her goodly sized breasts heaving within her bodice like the waves of a Southern Ocean squall, and pouted. For a simple child she was. This I liked greatly.

'Brutes! I'll die by mine own hand – though it be mortal sin to do so – before you take my Maidenhood!'

This protestation encouraged more laughter from my men. They hooted like the baboons of Ceylon.

The First Mate revealed his **eye socket** to her, provoking the lady to squealing and the men to more throaty laughter.

>> Life's better in **high-definition**. **Regain 20/20 vision** through **laser surgery** now! Go **here**. T&C's apply. (No refunds) <<

'Shall I strip her, Captain Bloodstem?' inquired he.

'No. Prepare her in my quarters.' I turned to my men. 'Your Captain will run her through aplenty tonight, eh boys?' They roared with delight.

Princess Aoife's green eyes broadened, and were most lovely. 'Tis truth but I did see the dash of a smile play on those lips, upon her hearing my name said.

'Captain … Bloodstem?'

'At your service, Madam,' I replied, removing my three-cornered hat and performing an exaggerated bow, in mimicry of the Fine Gentlemen of London.

'Your reputation precedes you, sir! They say you have ransacked twice-more Maidens than you have done British Frigates.'

I will confess that upon hearing the Princess Aoife recite my History, I suffered a Pang of Abasement – rather than the Sweetness of its forbidden Allure – for the first time in my awful **pirating** career.

>> Go **here** to watch **Pirates of the Caribbean: It Never Ends** now!
T&C's apply. (No refunds) <<

That first Pang – as I found later – would set me free from sin, and from Death unto Life.

'Aye, Lady,' said the first mate. 'My captain hath **Raped** his way through all the Indies.'

'Silence, Eel-Pie-Jack!' I snapped. Not wishing to appear out of humours, however – or frighten the Princess any more (for I had a sudden powerful desire to please her) – I subsequently ordered him, *sotto voce*, as the Italians say, to make up my quarters for dinner. 'The Princess and her Captain will walk about the poop deck the meanwhile,' I declared.

I offered her the crook of mine arm to hold, as if we were to perambulate the Hyde Park. She received it with surprising enthusiasm. Mine own Mast was set fairly upright within my breeches by this unexpected keenness of hers, causing me to walk with her in a most ungainly manner, rather like a poorly Victim of Urban Disease, such as the Polio. The softness of her skin, even the disturbances made by the breeze upon the hairs of her slender arm, also spoke much to my desire. Further – shame to confess! – my pirate soul was in calculations of how much more obliging she might be once we had dined.

There upon the poop deck did we watch the sun complete, with God's Grace, its diurnal path, spreading its heavenly fires across the evening sky. My lady Aoife gasped amazedly when she did glimpse the Wonder of the Green Ray, as the solar disk slipped beneath the watery edge of our Earth.

'Take off your eyeglasses, Captain,' said she, in the blue confidences of the Twilight, 'that I may discern any Goodness in your soul.'

I did as she commanded, so enchanted was I by her fair bobbed hair (which was very like Jean-Hervé's, our cabin boy) – she had cast the wretched auburn periwig into the sea as the sun retreated – by her own slate-green eyes, and by those pale rose-petalled lips which seemed forever upon the point of divulging a Divine Secret.

'Let us dine, Captain,' Princess Aoife whispered. 'And for afters, we shall dine upon one another.' A great flame did scorch me upon hearing this counterfeit-cannibal summons to love-making.

'Oh.' She said. 'And bring your crew in to watch us. This Princess requires an audienc – '

'Stop!'

Playlist stopped.

Waiting …

'…'

>> Don't delay! *Win 'Big Cash Prizes'* when you vote in this year's **BEST SEX EVER AWARDS**, Waylon43! **Vote here** for your **Favourite Room** – and share with your **friends**! T&C's apply. <<

'Go to LiveCam AoifeSEXXX.'

Loading …

Please wait …

Room 6:

AoifeSEXXX bunches her legs up under her chin and smiles. She sits on her bed, which is spread with a blue-striped duvet. She wears white knickers and a tight, grey T-shirt that emphasises the fact she is not wearing a bra. Her almost colourless fair hair is longer now. She wears a heavy blue eye shadow, and is sucking on a mauve lollipop. She removes the lollipop from her mouth and waves to the 20,341 fans of hers who are online right now.

'Permit audio.'

'-o boys!' says AoifeSEXXX to the LiveCam. 'How are you today?' She puts the lollipop back between her pale rose lips.

'I'm feeling prett-y horny today, let me tell you,' she says, gobbing over the words, the lollipop bulging her left cheek. 'Are you reading for some real, live action?'

User B0nerboy1984 is writing … 'u bet AoifeSEXXX!!!! luv ur pussy so muuccch'

'Aw, that's so sweet, B0nerboy84,' says AoifeSEXXX.

User Amerika4evah is writing … 'ur tits r so cute'

'And thank you, Amerika4evah! Remember, guys: it's 20 credits for a peep of my lil' boobs, 40 for pussy play. Hit my 100-credit target and you all get to see me use my favourite toy.' She picks up a bright blue, 11-inch marital aid which, to Waylon43, looks like a cross between a dildo and some kind of thermonuclear device. 'Say hello to Mr Electric Eel here.' She opens her eyes very wide, as if shocked or in the throes of religious awe.

User Amerika4evah is writing … 'u da best AoifeSEXXX I luv u'

User B0nerboy1984 is writing … 'fuk u i luv AoifeSEXX the best'

User Amerika4evah is writing … 'fuk u u homo … im AoifeSEXXs no1 luv'

AoifeSEXXX says, 'Now, now, boys! Any more of that and you'll be barred by the Moderator. I love all of you guys – and girls! – equally. All 20 thousand of you!' She twists the lollipop between thumb and forefinger. 'Hit my 100-credit target five times …' she begins.

User Waylon43 is writing … 'I love you, Aoife. It's me, Waylon. Please ca – '

User Waylon43 has been blocked by Room Moderator.

'Hit my target five times, guys, and you get to see me go to funkytown – with my pal here, Jean-Hervé!' Jean-Hervé, black hair to his waist, comes into view. At first, there are just his legs and penis, which swings from side to side, like finger wagged way back in the past by one of Waylon43's school teachers. He crouches down and waves hello at the LiveCam.

'Bienvenue, tout le monde!' says Jean-Hervé, with a very friendly smile.

User Waylon43 is writing … User Waylon43 has been blocked by Room Moderator.

AoifeSEXXX removes her T-shirt and knickers: 'Would you look at that, Jean: 100 credits already!' She blows a kiss. 'Here we go, sugarcubes!' AoifeSEXXX goes to plug in the Electric Eel. Jean-Hervé moves toward the LiveCam, puts his thumbs up and gives another friendly smile.

'Exit LiveCam AoifeSEXXX.'

>> Hey! Was that your **Favourite Room**, Waylon43? **Vote here** for your **Favourite Room** in this year's **BEST SEX EVER AWARDS** – and share with your **friends**! T&C's apply. <<

'Switch off Glasses.

>> **Manze's International** uses *only the very best* **Atlantic Rock Eels** in its **Jellied Eel Burgers**. Go **here** for the *perfect combination* of the freshness of the sea and the taste of chicken. T&C's apply. No refunds. <<

'Now. Switch off, now!
Glasses off.
'…
'…
'Glasses. On.'
Ping!
New playlist for you based on your History. Play now?
'No.'
Waiting for order …
'Go to … Go to GlassesCam 13/2/19, circa 10.55 am.'
Loading …

Room 7:
'So we've decided this is a good idea?' says AoifeSEXXX to Waylon43. They are tucked under a blue-striped duvet. They have just made love and are holding each other close. She speaks into his neck. He speaks into her

>> Hiya! Is this your **Favourite Room**, Waylon43? **Vote here** in this year's **BEST SEX EVER AWARDS** – and share with your **friends**! T&C's apply. <<

lush, auburn, **BelindaFyst** curls. She will perform acts on the internet to earn money, because they need rent cash, by Monday. They have decided that, given the **financial situation**, this is the best thing, the best course of action.

>> **Unexpected bill?** Get a **great value loan*** right now **through Lucratif.**
T&C's apply. *APR 14.5K% average. **Lucratif** is regulated by the Financial Services Advocacy. <<

Waylon43 will continue working at **Shoe Depot's** Coulsdon warehouse. At work, Waylon43's Glasses factor Best-Fulfilment-Route-Advice against Time-to-Find-Updates. AoifeSEXXX was fired after breaking her Glasses a third time. Glasses are an essential part of warehouse executing as well as being the premier consumer-info-social interface. **Shoe Depot** regrets that AoifeSEXXX has excluded herself from both an exciting career future at **Shoe Depot** and – in her free time – so many consumer-info-social opportunities. **Shoe Depot** is insistent that its generous loan schemes for Glasses, which, as stressed, offer a cavalcade of non-work consumer-info-social choices, must be paid in full.

'It's no big deal Waylon,' says AoifeSEXXX to Waylon43's neck. 'My time will be my own and the money's not bad. Anyway, I used to do it. When I was travelling. You just need a Home Cam. I quite like it, actually.'

The breath stops in Waylon43 for a couple of seconds.

'You what?'

'I've even got a handle: AoifeSEXXX. I can reactivate my old Room.'

'Excuse me?' Waylon43 releases AoifeSEXXX from his arms.

'Come on, Waylon. It's only sex. It doesn't mean much at all. We could do it in the Room *together*. The two of us. You won't believe the amount of people who dig that. Maybe *you* could quit **Shoe Depot**, too.'

'**No**. No way.'

>> *The cheapest and the best!* Order **any pair of shoes** direct to *your door* with **Shoe Depot**. Go **here**. T&C's apply. (No Refunds)
No cash? Refinance* with our Sister Corp **Lucratif**.
T&C's apply. *APR 14.5K% average. **Lucratif** is regulated by the Financial Services Advocacy. <<

'Most of them use their Glasses to enter Rooms. Just like you.'

'I don't want other men looking at you.'

AoifeSEXXX sits up, pulling the duvet over herself. 'Jesus. *You* look at other women all the time, don't you Waylon? With those Glasses. You never take them off in bed these days. Do I look like that fucking LiveCam queen now? Melinda, is it? Have you stuck her hair on me? What about her fake tits? Am I wearing them now?'

Waylon43 turns away, but does not take off his Glasses.

'I think I might as well do some Room Service as you're floating through them most of the time. We'd spend more time together. That's what I think.' AoifeSEXXX gets out of bed and puts her knickers and woollen leggings on.

At the bedroom door, she says, 'What's happening to us?'

'Pause.'

GlassesCam paused.

Glasses waiting for command …

'Zoom in to AoifeSEXXX. Medium close-up.'

Waylon43 reaches out to touch AoifeSEXXX, who is a little blurry because she is paused in mid-walk. His hand strokes the image tenderly. Waylon43 **strikes** himself **in the cheek**. **Twice**. **Hard**.

'I'm **sorry**, Aoife. Please **forgive me**.'

>> Make **The Bitch** pay! Go **here** for *safe*, sexy **Simulated Rape** with **Tru Ex-Girlfiends**. We use your **History** to compile a **Tru Avatar**! T&C's apply. (No Refunds) <<

Waiting for order …

'Go to LiveCam BelindaFyst.'

Loading …

Please wait …

Room 8:

BelindaFyst crouches on all fours on her bed. Her marvellous, *curvacious* backside is in the foreground, raised up at the HomeCam for the 200,321 fans online right now. She looks over her shoulder at her fans with an expression at once pained and amused, like she knows some secret Waylon43 doesn't. Her auburn hair curls down her back. She inserts several Love Bots in her bald vagina. Carly Rae Jepsen is soundtracking the show with her international smash hit single 'Call Me Maybe'.

'*I threw a wish in the well. Don't ask me, I'll never tell*,' sings Carly-Rae. '*I looked to you as it fell, and now you're in my way …*'

User onanthedestroyer is writing … 'fuck yeh set those bots to max Belinda!!!'

'*I'd trade my soul for a wish, pennies and dimes for a kiss …*'

User woriedaboutGvt is writing … 'da fuqin best'

'*Your stare was holdin', ripped jeans, skin was showin' …*'

User Waylon43 is writing … 'God.'

'Thank you, Waylon43!' says Belinda, eyes watering and teeth chattering from the Love Bots working inside her. 'But I think you mean Goddess!' Don't forget to vote for my **Room** in the **Best Sex Awards**.

'*Before you came into my life, I missed you so bad. I missed you so, so bad …*'

'Exit LiveCam BelindaFyst.'

>> Make **BelindFyst**'s wildest dreams come true, Waylon43, and she will make yours! **Vote here** to make her **Room** your **Favourite** in this year's **BEST SEX EVER AWARDS** – and share with your **friends**! T&C's apply. <<

'Go to LiveCam AoifeSEXXX.'
Loading …
LiveCam AoifeSEXXX unavailable. Room is offline.
'Aoife.
'Glasses. Off.'
Glasses off.
'…
'Glasses. On.'
Ping!
New playlist for you based on your History. Play now?
'Go to LiveCam AoifeSEXXX.'
Reloading …
LiveCam AoifeSEXXX unavailable. Room is offline.
'…
'Go to GlassesCam, 09/08/18, circa 1.20pm.'
Loading …
Please w–

Room 9:
Waylon43 and AoifeSEXXX are having lunch in the small cafeteria of Shoe Depot's Coulsdon warehouse. All the tables are taken so they stand by the windows. They eat their **Manze's paninis** in silence to the hubbub of conversation and the clatter of cutlery.

>> **Mmmm. Manze**'s fresh **Paninis**. Go **here** for delivery to your door! T&C's apply. (No Refunds) <<

Waylon43 is thinking about saying something to her – to mention the fact that they haven't even got a seat for the break; or maybe how he likes her blond, almost colourless bob. They are about to speak to one another for the first time.
'Pause.'

Waiting …

'Extract all audio and images of AoifeSEXXX from this Room.'

Complying …

'Make New Room from Playlist based on my History: **Connemara** beach. Construct avatar of AoifeSEXXX using **Tru Ex** account.

Complying …

>> **Warning**, Waylon43! You have just six credits left in your **Tru Ex-Girlfriends** account following purchase of **Avatar Creation Bits** for **AoifeSEXXX**. *Don't let her slip away when you leave the Room*! Buy more credits now by going **here**! T&C's apply. (No Refunds) <<

Do you wish to dress AoifeSEXXX in French basque /off-white wedding dresss / fabulous hot pants / nun's habit / or go ***here*** *for more sexy ideas?*

'No'

Finishing Room … Do you require new audio? (Suggestions: Clair de Lune by Claude Debussy, We Have All the Time in the World by John Barry, Hey Babe by Neil Young?)

'No. Leave original audio entire. Make Room Scenario summer's day.'

Room 10:

Waylon43 and AoifeSEXX stand on the immaculate sands of a Connemara beach, at the very edge of world. They wear the brown and black combat fatigues of Shoe Depot warehouse executives, and they are munching on **paninis**. The waves slush peacefully against the shore on a beautiful, still June day. Every colour – every blue, green and white – is vivid and fresh. There is the faint smell of manure mixed with the sharp iodine of the rolling ocean. An ancient farmer is taking his herd of white and ochre cattle down to paddle in the Atlantic. They are lowing, but make no sound. All around AoifeSEXXX and Waylon43 are the sounds of warehouse executives at their break. Knives and forks scrap plates. Denise, the Italian dinner lady, calls out meal numbers.

Waylon43 and AoifeSEXXX stand together on this beach. He really wants to say something to her, but doesn't. He doesn't. The Back-to-Work-Countdown at the right edge of his Glasses informs him that he has -02.33 minutes to click in at the Work Area.

AoifeSEXXX says, 'Well. This is great. Nowhere to sit again. I'm exhausted. How about you?'

'Yeah. Me also.' They have to shout to make themselves heard over the audio of the cafeteria. The waves on the beach almost touch their study black combat boots.

'I've seen you on the other side of my Area. You're next along, right?' she cries.

'Right.'

'Aoife. Pleased to meet you.' She offers her hand.

Before they shake hands, Waylon43 wipes his fingers on his **Manze's** serviette. 'Waylon. Nice to meet you. I've seen you, too. You always look on top of your Fulfilments.'

'I wish! But thanks … I guess. I'm running behind today. I feel like shit. In fact, you always look like you're gonna fall over when you're executing yours.'

'Yeah,' he shouts, inserting a self-deprecatory chuckle.

Aoife laughs, 'No, it's nice. It's cute … I've often thought how cute you seem over there, Waylon.'

They listen to the cafeteria noise.

'Sometimes I feel like crying, you know,' she says.

'It's not great here, is it?'

>> Time to relax. Come to **Connemara**! Go **here** for more info.
T&C's apply. (No refunds) <<

'No. Not that, really. Sometimes I just feel like it. Why not? I mean, why not cry a bit sometimes – just for the hell of it. Just because you can, you know.'

'Ha. I don't know about that.' Back-to-Work-Countdown reads -00.39 seconds. The farmer is wading in the water with his cows. The sky is unclouded. There are skylarks flitting in the air. They emit no song. Denise calls out another meal number.

'Maybe it's these Glasses,' shouts AoifeSEXXX. 'They're useful, sure, but I reckon they damage our eyes, you know. And, of course, our dear **Shoe Depot** knows exactly where you are with them on.'

Back-to-Work-Countdown has started flashing red: -00.15 seconds.

Waylon43 does not move off to his Area.

'You know what, Waylon?' says AoifeSEXXX.

'What, Aoife?'

'I've had it with these things for today.' She removes her Glasses, and spins them around on one of their tortoise-shell arms. She drops them to the floor. They rattle on the white sand, which sounds like concrete. She giggles and looks at Waylon43. She has slate-green eyes studded with greyish flecks. Waylon43 asks himself whether they are **Irish** eyes.

She shakes her fair hair and says, 'That's better! Only my second pair so far.' Then she stamps the Glasses into the sand. They shatter. The cafeteria has abruptly gone quiet. The cows splash in the shallows on the other side of the little bay.

Waylon43 feels himself swallow in embarrassment or excitement – he can't figure out which. This – what she has done – and AoifeSEXXX herself – he likes. Greatly.

'Go on. Let's see your eyes too, Waylon,' she says. 'I can see them behind your Glasses, sure – brown, aren't they? – but I want to see what you look like without them. Can you take them off for me, so I can see you? Come on! Let's see what you're like.'

His thumb and forefinger on the left arm of his Glasses, Waylon43 hesitates. The Back-to-Work Countdown is flashing -00.00 in red at the edge of his vision. AoifeSEXXX is reaching out to him across the blinding white sands to take them off anyway.

'Pause.'

Waiting …

>> Psst! Sorry to interrupt you *Sexy Beasts* – but it's **time to vote** for this year's **THE BEST SEX EVER AWARDS**! **Vote here** to make this **Room** your **Favourite** – and share with your **friends**! T&C's apply. <<

SARAH BURTON

Paint

Yesterday when my wife came home from work without even taking her coat off she slapped a paint chart on the kitchen table and said 'I want the staircase this colour'.

She had ringed a square of colour. It didn't have a name, just a number, but it looked kind of limey.

'For the walls?' I tried not to sound sceptical. What she calls my 'knee-jerk negativity' doesn't go down well.

'No, the walls will be white. All the walls will be white. This is for the staircase itself.'

No, not limey, more like the vivid snot of a small child with a streaming cold.

'It's pistachio,' she said.

'How do you know? It's only got a number.'

'It just is. That's what that colour is called.' She sighed. 'Don't say you don't like it.'

So I didn't.

My wife runs London's most successful publicly funded art gallery. You don't argue with a minor national treasure on matters of taste. Still, it matters to her that I like the choices she makes. And I found, however hard I tried – and it surprised me – that I couldn't even pretend to like G1693 and certainly didn't want it up three flights of stairs.

'Imagine you had a hangover and you had to negotiate this,' I waved the chart, 'before you could even get a glass of water. It's inhumane.'

'You exaggerate,' she said, putting on the kettle. 'You always exaggerate. That's your trouble.'

I looked at her back and then at the chart. Did I love her enough to put up with it? Of course I did, but that didn't mean I had to put up with it. 'It's almost fluorescent… like… dayglo green,' I said. 'It's a punk colour. It's hurting my eyes just looking at this tiny bit of it.'

She spun round smiling as though she had just thought of something wonderful. 'You'll never guess what!' she said.

'Tell me,' I said, in a way which I hoped suggested I slightly regretted leaving the subject of the green but was willing to do so if it made her happy. That was too much information for just two words to carry, so it probably sounded just ordinary.

'What do you know about Degenerate Art?'

'Nothing. Except it's to do with Hitler.'

'Yes,' she said, 'it's to do with Hitler.' And she sat on the end of the kitchen table with her cup of tea and began what I knew would be something like a story and I love it when she does that, except when I'm in a hurry, which I wasn't.

'It's 1937. He's been in power for four years and he is very worried about art. He's alarmed at the rise of expressionism – it's ugly, disturbing, doesn't make sense – and he thinks Germans need reminding what "good" art is…' here she made that little quotation sign with her fingers, 'you know the kind of thing: happy farmers, mothers with babies, noble nordic warriors – all blonde of course –'

'"Blood and soil."'

'What? Oh yes, yes. And some like his own paintings – the ones that didn't get him into art school – chocolate boxy so-called realism, but none of this modern nonsense. So he builds a new gallery in Munich to put it all in – along with nudes – male and female, impossibly idealised – *so many nudes* it's almost pornographic. Anyway he calls this The Great German Art Exhibition and a million people go to see it.'

'Sounds like a great day out,' I said.

'But that's not enough. It's almost as if "good" art is not "good" enough to stand on its own merits, so he needs, also, to remind the people what "bad" art is. So what does he do? Just down the road he opens *another* exhibition with all the "bad" stuff in. He calls it "Degenerate Art" just so people know. The Nazis had already removed thousands of "degenerate" works from museums and galleries – Picassos, Matisses, Chagalls, Mondrians, Van Goghs –'

'Van Goghs?'

She nodded without breaking her flow, ' – and now they put the mostly German ones in the exhibition. You look at the catalogue now and it's a roll-call of the great modernists: Klee, Kokoscha, Kandinsky, Beckman, Nolde, Grosz, Dix, Kirchner, Ernst… And it's almost as if "bad" art is not "bad" enough to discredit itself – a poor venue is chosen deliberately – the rooms are much smaller than in the other gallery, the walls are deliberately overcrowded with paintings – some not even in frames, some hung a bit wonky, some of the abstracts were even hung upside down. And as if *that's* not bad enough, and people *still* don't get the point that it's all trash, the walls are covered with text ridiculing the paintings – stuff like "An insult to German womankind" and "Nature as seen by sick minds" – one room that was just abstracts was labelled "The Insanity Room". Oh, and I forgot to say, they put the prices up on the walls that galleries had paid for these "monstrosities", just to get people really angry and disgusted with it. And all the art was supposed to be by Jews and Bolsheviks of course. And *three* million people went to see that one.'

She pulled her iPad out of her bag and showed me a short black and white film of people at the exhibition. It was just as she'd described and though I couldn't understand the Nazi propaganda neatly graffitied on the walls it did all look a mess. There was no sound on the film and the visitors looked baffled, rather than angry or disgusted, or inscrutable, and drew back when they became aware of the camera. One man covered his face.

'So,' she said when it was over. 'Guess what.'

I couldn't.

'I'm going to recreate the exhibition.'

The idea sat in the air between us for a moment.

'Which one?' I asked.

She stared at me, mouth open, as her mind rapidly recalibrated. 'Oh… my…God. You are a genius.' She jumped off the table and kissed me. 'I'll recreate *both* exhibitions!'

It had legs, certainly. The secret of her success is her originality in planning exhibitions, marrying unexpected curators with unusual themes. I had been lukewarm about them all at first, worrying that this time she'd gone too far, assumed too much. All had been standout sellout hits. I had been wrong. I didn't want to be wrong again.

'That's brilliant,' I said, realising that this time I had actually had a hand in the brilliance. She hadn't thought of mounting *both* exhibitions, had she? That was my doing. I started to glow with anticipated pride. I imagined her on Front Row, '…and then my *husband* said "why don't you recreate *both* exhibitions?"'

'But so far I've only thought out the Degenerate one. And everything must be as close to the original as it can possibly be. The Nazi graffiti, the pictures all askew and cramped together. And the actors. Oh, darling, I didn't tell you that they actually hired actors to walk round the exhibition mingling with the punters and criticising the artworks. We'll do that too.'

This was getting better and better, like one of those plays where you walk round a warehouse in the dark bumping into things. A happening. Event theatre, is it called now? Anyway, everyone likes it. It's cutting edge stuff, this.

'Hang on, major problem.' I couldn't help myself. 'You'll never get the original works. They'll all be worth a fortune now.'

'Already started checking that and it's tricky. Some are lost – but we could hang empty frames – that's always powerful. It will cost a bomb in insurance and logistics will be a nightmare. But it's doable.'

'When you say "lost"...'

'Oh, some sold, some burnt by the Nazis – they burnt a lot, ritualistically, like the books – some kept by the Nazis, some just lost.'

'Couldn't you display reproductions? With an explanation?'

She thought and nodded and made a note in her iPad. 'Possibility,' she said.

'What if...' I ventured, but I'd had one good idea, so why not hazard another? 'What if you didn't hang *any* of the originals but hung *all* reproductions, and then had a ritualistic public burning of everything at the end of the exhibition?'

She gave me the same look as she had when I made my first brilliant suggestion. 'To complete the story...' she said. 'That is utter gold, sheer coruscating genius.' She jumped up and kissed me again.

'It would be better to have them in two different venues, of course,' she continued planning. 'We can recreate the original dimensions of the Degenerate gallery rooms in the Turbine Hall at Tate Modern and The Great German Art Exhibition will be splendid at Tate Britain. And instead of the big vertical banners outside the old Tate we'll have giant red flags with swastikas on. And the guides will be in uniform. I'll have to look that up – would they be SS?' She rapidly typed another note. 'God, this is exciting.'

I suddenly felt terribly sick.

'I've just realised something awful,' I said. 'Don't you see who would come to your exhibitions?'

She looked up at me, uncomprehending, and then disappointment stained her face. I was pissing all over her dreams again, but this time she knew I was right.

She put her hand to her mouth suddenly, unconsciously, like a dismayed child. 'Neo-Nazis,' she said. 'Of course.' She thought some more, and the thoughts grew. 'Of course they would.' She leaned against the table. A few moments passed like this.

I got up and put my arms around her. I was surprised to feel her body shuddering slightly. Surely she wasn't crying? 'You have good ideas, darling,' I said, prepared to give her all the credit now. 'The best. It's just the others. Other people. They're not all good. Not like you.'

She squeezed me gratefully, then stepped back, sniffing. She pulled her phone out of her bag.

'So I'll order the paint for the stairs, OK?' She kissed me once more, and started dialling while she was still walking out of the room.

MELANIE CHENG

Allomother

Sunday nights are for planning. I search the internet for the latest exhibits, concerts and other kid-friendly events. We've been to the core attractions: the museum, the botanical gardens, the children's farm, the gallery. We've sampled babycinos and avocado smash at all but the most pretentious cafes. Sometimes I don't plan anything at all. I plan not to plan – because too much structure can suffocate creativity in a child – and we do silly things like make nappies for Dolly from the fallen leaves in my backyard.

Monday nights are for cooking. I bake homemade treats for our outings. Healthy snacks like apricot muesli bars and savoury muffins made with organic pumpkin and goat's cheese. There has to be something to counteract the frozen rubbish that gets dished up at home. *Snap frozen*, her mother corrects me, but she is just defending the time she spends on the couch, watching back-to-back episodes of *House of Cards*.

Tuesday nights are for packing. Or rather checking that my oversized, waterproof handbag is adequately stocked. Because, when it comes to kids – and Molly in particular – you can never be too prepared. Every so often I get caught out and have to add another item to my list. It's an organic thing, my list, a little like my muesli bars. *Two packets of Wiggles bandaids, one tube of Cancer Council approved nano-free kids sunscreen, a hat, a cardy, a spare pair of undies, a BPA-free water bottle, a Tupperware box with aforementioned organic snacks, face towels, Molly's second favourite Barbie doll (Candy, with the blue biro-coloured hair) and my camera.*

* * *

I have one photo. Jules and Mick took everything else – the ultrasound images and DVDs, even the positive pregnancy test I dipped in my urine. It's a selfie taken in the bathroom mirror, with one hand cupping my belly. The phone covers my face. Only my mouth is showing. I am wearing a grey maternity top from Kmart and a pair of black trackie dacks covered in lint. There are no identifying features. No scars or beauty spots or tattoos of ex-lovers' names. Nothing to prove that it is me. It could be anyone.

* * *

'I want to see the ephelants.'

We are in the monkey enclosure. A female is nursing her newborn; two young chimps are catapulting from tree to tree; and a large male is lying on the platform-cum-stage, juggling his salmon-pink testicles.

Molly sucks her thumb. She is an elephant person, like her mother. Jules brought me a sandalwood one once, as a last minute gift, at Koh Samui Airport. But that was a long time ago. Back when she and Mick had money to travel. Before IVF, and the miscarriages. Before varicose veins, and Molly.

'Dara's waiting for me.'

Dara is the new elephant calf. One of three conceived at the zoo.

'His name means star,' Molly says, as we turn our back on the monkeys. 'Like me!'

'That's right,' I say, genuinely impressed. 'Yours means star of the sea.'

I don't mention the Hebrew meaning – and the reason Jules and Mick chose it in the end. *Molly. Diminutive of Mary: the wished-for one.*

* * *

They took vial after vial of blood. I was terrified but I needn't have been. My hormone levels were *within normal limits* and my uterus wasn't *hostile* – who knew organs could be hostile? – like my sister's. It was the proof I had been searching for all these years that I was better than her. But the victory didn't give me the joy I thought it would. I didn't feel like I'd won anything.

* * *

At strategic points around the zoo there are candy coloured signs spouting facts about the animals:

Did you know that elephant society has a female-led structure that is often called matriarchal? The oldest female is the matriarch. She determines the group's movements.

I try to explain the words to Molly – to convey the complexity of these awesome beasts – but she just hops on one foot and screams that she needs to wee.

* * *

It wasn't until I was being wheeled into theatre that any of us believed I might actually die.

'You'll be fine.' The anaesthetist said but I didn't trust him. He was too good-looking to be a doctor.

I watched the painful shrink of Mick and Jules' faces as they pulled me along the corridor. They didn't wave – that would have been too much like farewell – they just stood very still. Only then did I see myself as they did: a vessel for their magic bean. For the first time, clutching each other as if they might drown in the linoleum sea, they looked the part: a mummy and a daddy.

* * *

I am drinking a watery cappuccino at the zoo cafeteria. Molly is under my chair, feeding discarded chips to a one-legged pigeon. It is three o'clock and the café is full. I scan the tables, priding myself on being able to pick the parents from the non-parents. The parents are the ones checking email on their smartphones while their toddler eats marshmallows off the floor. It's the Nannas and Pops and Aunties and Uncles who hang, bright-eyed, on every mispronounced word, confident they will soon be rewarded with a flash of wisdom or comedic genius. Like when Molly compares the mole on my neck to a sultana, or asks me questions I can't answer, like whether fish sleep and if they do how do I know if they never close their eyes?

* * *

Did you know that the main function of the family unit is the protection of baby elephants? The greater the number of females looking after a calf, the greater its chance of survival.

* * *

I looked at Jules and Mick across the expanse of polished mahogany.

'Just a formality hun.'

The lawyer was an ageless Chinese woman who could pass for forty or fourteen. She nudged the thirty-page document towards me.

At birth, the Surrogate will relinquish the Child(ren) to the Biological Father and Biological Mother, and the Biological Father and Biological Mother will assume all parental rights and responsibilities for the Child(ren) from that time forward.

Twenty weeks. She was the length of a banana. Her ears were perfectly formed. I had just started to feel her dart like a slippery fish inside me.

'We wanted to wait.' Jules said, as if reading my mind.

'To make sure it was viable.' Mick explained.

'It?' I snapped and Mick went white. We had found out the sex at the last scan.

'*She*.'

Jules shook her head. The lawyer pulled a pen from her breast pocket. One of those old-fashioned fountain pens with a reservoir and a nib. She placed it in a ceremonious diagonal across the paper.

'I'm not going to steal your child.'

'Of course not.' Jules said but the baby-faced lawyer disagreed.

'Kids do strange things to people.'

I looked at my sister's stony face and her husband's blotchy, patchwork one. I felt a flutter – the flap of tiny arms perhaps – in the fleshy space below my bellybutton. I picked up the pen.

'They sure do.'

* * *

Dad took me and Jules to the zoo once. I must have been about thirteen. It was a big deal, coming down on the train from Bendigo for the day. We were celebrating Jules getting picked for the under 15s netball team. Mum had to work but Dad, being a teacher, was off for the school holidays.

I don't think they had elephant calves at the zoo in those days. I don't remember much about the animals to tell the truth. Mainly I remember how a couple of boys with skateboards stared at Jules on the train. She had just grown breasts – firm things that tented her t-shirt like a couple of smuggled plums – and I remember how she stared out the window, with those long hairless legs neatly tucked beneath her bottom, and how everything in the carriage rattled, it seemed, except for her.

* * *

Did you know that baby elephants can have more than one mummy? Sometimes, a female cow who is not quite ready to have her own baby, looks after her younger siblings and cousins. The practice is known as allomothering. The female is the allomother.

* * *

It is standing room only at the elephant enclosure. Molly is up on my shoulders. The calf, his eyes red with fright, cowers beneath the belly of an elderly cow. I'm reminded of Nanna's oak dining table and the long days Jules and I spent playing beneath it. A keeper holds up a loudspeaker. He informs us that an elephant pregnancy lasts two years. There are gasps from the audience. Mothers mainly. *Imagine that,* they say, and laugh and rub their deflated bellies.

* * *

'You can use this,' Jules said, uncoiling a bandage. 'Or take the drugs.'

My hands crept up towards my breasts. They were hard and lumpy, like jackfruit.

'You wrap it tight as you can,' she said, studying the crepe between her fingers. 'Harriet's doula swears by it.'

I took the bandage and retreated to the bedroom. Jules had never asked me to express and I had never offered, even though we both knew it would be the best thing for Molly. I suspect it would have undone her: another thing my body could do that hers couldn't.

It took everything not to scream. Milk seeped through the flesh-coloured fabric, creating brown stains above my nipples. It hurt like buggery, as my mother would say, but pain was what I wanted. I'd been asleep for the emergency C-section and had no memory of a labour. I needed to feel the tear of tissues, the gush of blood, the shear of placenta from womb. Because I always thought it should be hideous – agonizing to the point of torture – it being the final cleavage of a child from its mother.

* * *

In the car on the way home I dissect the day's events.

Did you have fun?

What was your favourite part?

Did you enjoy seeing all the animals?

Molly provides monosyllabic answers between long sucks of her dirty thumb. She isn't like me, always looking in the rear view mirror. She is focused on the road ahead, craning to see what lies around the next bend.

As we park outside her house, Molly sits up straight in her booster seat. Once out, she holds my hand for a millisecond before breaking away to tear down the driveway. I watch her bang on the front door with two fists and stand on tippytoes to reach the handle. I can still feel her hot little hand in mine as I see Julie's long silhouette in the doorway. She can't get inside fast enough. The house swallows her, hungrily.

JOANNA M HERRMANN

Ice Injuries: Halvmaneoya Island, Winter 1970

And so it begins. The first whiteout of the season, twelve weeks in. Wiping the slim blade of his skinning knife, Lars staggers slightly in the fragile circle of light cast by his storm lamp. He nudges into the pelt he has just hung, breathing in fat-membranes and flecks of fur. There are only two of them across the entire Archipelago this year: Sivertsen out on Hornsund, and him here on Halvmaneoya. His half-moon island, his island of bones.

Painstakingly he starts to check the skins that make up the winter's lean quota. He needs to make sure they are in order. He also needs to unhinge the automated spring-gun while he can reach it. He knows it will be days, perhaps weeks, before the weather subsides and he can hunt again. Running his hand along the length of the pelts, Lars satisfies himself that there's enough air between them. His fingertips search out the line of each jaw, alert to any irregularities, every tooth carrying a charge of dense cold against his touch. He senses the quiet presence of each animal. Their skins carry a collective odour of stale fat and blood, muted by the extreme cold. This indignity pains him, as does the fact that they are jostled together like silent commuters on an urban train. Shoulder to shoulder they hang: yellowed and stiff. He feels an urge to retch, but concentrates on the slow movements required to muffle his face in his visor. The wind is moving in at the northern tip of the headland, raising the fierce, intermittent whine of bones restless on their nylon cords. Hollow, frost-worked, they moan just at the edge of his hearing in their thousands. Nothing decays on Halvmaneoya. Over the decade that he's been trapping on the island, Lars has collected the bones of hunted bears and threaded them onto lengths of rope attached to the exterior walls of his cabin. Polar bear bones are his only company.

Stepping out of the lean-to, he realises he may be too late to reach the set gun, but he has to take the risk. He tries to bring the gun into focus against the blur of flakes. The pole it is mounted on is three times his height, the only object of any significance on the vertical axis for miles.

The bears are drawn to it by their curiosity. If they get close enough, the trigger is activated, and with any luck the bullet will give a clean kill. Often, however, set guns are messy and undignified dispensers of death. Looking up he can just distinguish a ragged shape fluttering from the top of the pole. A blackened scrap of skin has frozen there like an obscene flag. In front of it, flurries of snow have left a pristine skim across shadowy blotches of stale blood. Lars can't allow the possibility of a bear being wounded without him being able to reach it and kill it outright. That happened once, in his second season. A female bear set off the gun and the bullet took away the side of her head. When he found her Lars didn't know how many hours she had been walking in circles in the snow. He dreams about her still.

Momentarily the fluttering of the scrap of skin at the top of the pole ceases and the wind drops. Lars is alert instantly, straining his senses to register any movement or change in the midday gloom. The shift in the Polar night is a month away, and Lars imagines he has already seen the darkness stretching and thinning. He senses, rather than hears, a slight creaking in the snow behind him. For eight days there have been no bears. Eight haunted days. In a normal season this would have warned him of approaching bad weather, but this is not a normal season. His ribcage constricts as he struggles to draw breath silently. He has no revolver with him, only the skinning knife, cold against his palm. In his dream the wounded bear walks ahead of him, the right hand side of her head blown away. Always she leads him along the same route, towards a place that he knows is Hell. Hell is waiting for him. He knows it in his soul.

He is fascinated by the tiny nails in the soles of his mother's shoes. She is kneeling in the pew in front of him. Lars peers through a gap in the woodwork, his hands over his eyes as if he is praying. Red sunlight filtering through the ornate church window illuminates the dust on the scuffed leather. The dust is white from the chalk path they take from the house. His mother is praying in a quiet whisper. After the service they make their way home along the same path.

'Oh how beautiful, Lars,' she exclaims as he makes darting forays into the pasture to pick her a primrose or an anenome. Looking back at her he notes the way the chalk rises in puffs of dust from her heels. Her skirt sways rhythmically from side to side. In his excitement he careers down a grassy knoll, tripping over his ungainly feet, and falls into a low-creeping shrub. Cradled at its base are three blue eggs. He breathes the scent of earth warmed by early sunshine, presses his palm against a clutch of delicate pebbles, root sinew, the ineffectual down of a fallen thistle.

'Oh Lars, this is a piece of heaven,' his mother exclaims softly over the egg nestled in her cupped hand. She is squatting at the side of the path, her crimson skirt tucked under her thighs like a child playing marbles in the playground. Her other hand rests on a tussock of coarse grass scattered with rabbit droppings. In the distance the islands sit like long whales in their own skeins of haze.

'A piece of spring heaven,' she sighs at the egg lying as quietly on her palm as a stone on a cool river bed.

The weather is turning, blowing into his back. A storm from the north-eastern quarter is always dangerous. Lars tries to gather his thoughts, peering into the darkness and sharpening his focus. Men have been lost, yards from their shelters, in north-easterlies. He will have to abandon de-activating the gun. He lifts his head and tests the air as a bear might. Somewhere under the wind he can just make out the plangent chord of the bones. As he begins to feel his way, step by step, towards the cabin, he lists the things he has to collect from the store:
Matches
Tins
Salt
Paper
Tea.
Matches
Tins
Salt
Paper
Tea.

The list is a buoy, and he clings to it, keeping his mind afloat. A funnel of air creates a spinning tower of snow just ahead of him. He pauses as it veers away to his left. The snow is piling in drifts at his feet even as he tries to walk. An arrow of pain from the wind's assault burns its trajectory through his being. Wild snowflakes are driving at his eyes, scalding his lashes. Nothing settles. His vision creates phantom shapes in the blocks of shadow as shifting outlines form and dissolve. Lars has no fear – a quality he shares with Sivertsen – but there is a stubborn instinct to survive. 'Survival is the poetry of the Arctic,' Sivertsen once told him. Lars flexes his left fist, feels the reassuring chill of the skinning knife's blade against his palm. The indigenous people say spirits travel on a gale from the North, and Lars believes them. Northerlies should blow as cold as ice, but when he hears his Winter-Child, her song is warm like breath, and soft where it curls in at the back of the storm.

'Lars, why weren't you in your bed last night?' His mother's face is wearing an expression of mild astonishment. The morning sunlight is shining through the long kitchen window. Her hands are white with flour. Flour dust floats in a sunbeam above her head.

'I was out.' He can't lie to anyone, least of all his mother. He pours coffee from an enamel pot into his white cup with its chipped handle.

'Out?' There is an inflection of pain in her voice.

'Yes. I was in the woods. The Fredriksen girls were there. I followed them.'

'I see,' his mother picks up the ball of dough she was kneading and pulls at it distractedly. 'Did they ask you to follow them?'

'No.'

The Fredriksen family spend every summer on the island, as Lars and his mother do. They're a familiar sight, foraging for wild food, chopping wood for the stove or tacking around the shore in their little skiff. Remote and self-sufficient, Lars often comes across the three girls returning from an expedition into the woods, their legs torn by thorns, or streaks of wild berry juice daubed on their angular faces. A month ago he began tracking their camps. He watched them as they goaded each other to jump higher and higher over their spruce fires, or as they urinated in spots around the patch of woodland they had cleared. The sight of those white areas of flesh glimmering in the soft light of a summer night was a glimpse into a world he could barely understand. He pushed his fingers into the layer of fallen leaves and needles on the forest floor to cause himself pain. Until now his mother had no idea that he wasn't in his bed. He tastes his coffee without milk, its bitterness excites him.

'Marta Fredriksen's coming to see me this evening.'

His mother drops the dough onto the kitchen table, prods it with a slender finger before wiping both her hands on her apron.

'Lars, that's lovely,' she enunciates the words slowly, as if she is weighing each one with care. 'Will she eat with us?'

'Yes.' He can't believe he's saying this. Marta, the youngest of the Fredriksen girls, is going to pay him a visit. He will be close enough to smell her, to catch the warmth of her breath. Marta, whom he has watched from a distance for years. Marta, whose hair is the spun light of daybreak. She wants to sit at a table and share food with him. He is dizzy with the unreality of this thought.

His mother walks a couple of paces around the table and reaches out to touch him on the cheek with the back of her hand. Lars sits back slightly so that her fingers can't make contact. She pulls her red apron hastily over her head, drops it onto the battered settle that was made for the house by her father and steps out into the sunlit yard.

Twenty-four hours on and the storm is still in the north-east. The hissing of the primus stove is a counterpoint to the uneven shrieking of the wind. The snow is banked against the back wall of the cabin like an iceberg. Lars has been in his bunk for fifteen hours. Marooned. Out across the snowfields he can hear chunks of ice crashing and sparring. His limbs ache. He is malnourished, he knows. On Halvamaneoya he pays his body the minimum of attention. All the men are the same, sharing a common disdain for their physical selves. He and Sivertsen sat out a north-easterly together in his second season. That whiteout lasted thirteen days. 1961. The year his daughter was born. The weather crew had mocked him when he and Sivertsen arrived on the station in October.

'Hey, Lars, you gave Marta a baby at last? Sivertsen told me when he was on the radio last week. When's she due?' Jonas, the chief meteorologist was giggling. He was a tall, spare man in his early forties.

'December the twenty-first,' Sivertsen answered for Lars, shrugging his shoulders slightly and looking at his boots. He knew Lars didn't like to talk about his home life

'So it was a good first week home this spring?' Jonas giggled again. Lars winced at these crude remarks. 'Marta's a beautiful woman. You're lucky Lars, and she doesn't drink does she? Birgit drinks too much. She didn't drink when we first met, always mineral water when we were out. I admired her for it. She blames the loneliness, and trying to manage the kids on her own. And the kids, I don't know how to talk to them when I'm there. They call me old bear.'

'Hey, Jonas, come on. I've seen you with your kids. You're great together,' said Otto earnestly. He was the youngest of the research crew, just out of university.

'Perhaps. This season's getting to me. It's different. The trappers are all cut-throat, apart from you two,' Jonas gestures at Lars and Sivertsen.

'Like a different world. And Birgit is changing. Perhaps we're getting older. Drifting apart.'

'Listen to him now,' Sivertsen looked up from the bottle of beer he had been cradling. 'Listen to him. Old bear! How old are you? Forty-one, forty-two?' He roared with laughter. 'Pack it all up. Go home. Mend your life with Birgit and the children.' He wiped the back of his hand across his mouth. 'Leave. Go and grow vegetables on your plot. Anything.'

Jonas was looking steadily at Sivertsen, his body hunched into an ill-fitting jumper. Lars noticed that Jonas' hair was thinning. A big man, but nothing bear-like about him.

'Don't. Don't tease me.'

'I'm not.' Sivertsen belched unapologetically.

'I can't just go home.'

'Why not?'

'I don't really know them, my family, and I don't know whether I can give this up. I don't mean just the money, I mean time here. You know how it is.'

'The Arctic?' Sivertsen boomed, slamming his bottle down on the crate that served as a table. 'You give it up, or you stand a good chance of dying here. That's the way it works. Look at you, you're already half way there.'

It was true. He and Sivertsen had just arrived, looked solid compared to the crew who had been on the station for four months. Lars considered Sivertsen's mane of white hair in the sulphurous glare of the cabin lamp and felt again the affection that bound him to the older man over the trapping season. It was a slender thread of warmth stitched through the textured darkness of the winter. Sivertsen had taught him the art of skinning a bear and how to read the weather. Sivertsen was fifty that season, twenty years his senior, had been on the sealing boats for a decade before he started trapping bears.

'Well, congratulations Lars. A baby for you and Marta! It's been a long time coming.' Jonas was grimacing obscenely behind Otto. Lars pulled his cuffs down over his wrists, a nervous gesture. On his left cuff was a faint line of tailor's chalk, grey-white against the deep blue of the cloth where Marta had measured him for a new jacket the evening before he left. He had submitted vacantly to her directions, sensing the unfamiliar swell of her stomach as she leant against him. 'You're already gone, aren't you?' she asked, the envelope where she had scrawled the dimensions of his torso crumpled in her left hand.

Already gone. The bud of his child, brushing his shoulder as Marta took his measurements. Lars forces himself up onto an elbow in his bunk, grief sharp as a claw in memory. Islands of colour float into his field of vision. A patchwork quilt, green hand-knitted socks. He sinks back. Colour is a wound binding him to that other world. Marta sat on the porch through the length of the entire summer that she was pregnant, sewing the quilt. Marta's world holds together with stitches and colour. It's a world of refuse collections, solid furniture, street lighting. Another world altogether. He touches the quilt lightly, in awe of the texture of the cloth, running his fingers along the stitches in each neatly applied motif. How can it be that they ever conceived a child? Lars Larsen and Marta Fredriksen? He can still feel the solid pressure of Marta's body moving beneath him that first afternoon home in the spring of 1961. Her breasts pushed close against his rib cage, her subtle odour of earth, of clove, of warmth. The soft shoots of her body were almost plant-like, viscous, that cleft in her, remarkable. He had watched her body change over the months before he left for Halvmaneoya with the curiosity of a biologist. The sight of her darkening nipples and the long line of hair defining itself from her navel to her pubis made him uneasy. She planted herbs and vegetables in their tiny allotment. Radish, dill and mint. From the intensity of his hunger Lars hallucinates the sudden pungency of dill and sour cream on new potatoes. He can't bear the grief that his daughter will never know these tastes, will never feel the texture of the garden's heavy clay soil. He imagines her fingers delving amongst flint and worms and clods of earth. Within a month of him returning for a second season, she was dead. He didn't know for eight weeks. He had no radio. Then as now. Why the need in him to be always out of reach?

'Lars, you move further and further away,' his mother tying her hair up into a loose knot as she gets ready to go to work in the city library. 'I don't want to know everything, I can't know everything, but I can see that you're suffering.' She slips her feet into her blue slingback shoes and runs her fingers round her heels, looking up at him as she bends. Her silk shirt rides up her back slightly. 'The days are gone when I could make things better for you, but I'm still here, don't shut me out.' Her cheeks are flushed as she looks up at him, her green eyes bright with perplexed tears. He watches her slight figure in its grey woollen coat recede along the street. As she turns the corner to wait by the bus stop he smashes his fist into the kitchen wall. The skin on the knuckle of his index finger splits open.

He needs to move, and forces himself to get up and take the billy can from the stove. He places the pan on the tea chest that serves as a sideboard and pauses, listening intently. The bones are silent, stifled by banks of snow that have driven against the cabin, even on the south side. The wind is turning capricious, and Lars can hear the eerie jangling of crystallised ice particles skidding across the surface of the sheet ice. He wipes out his mug and spoons a measure of coffee into a battered pot. Black grains spill into his unsteady palm. Making coffee once a day is a ritual that keeps him anchored to the earth. As the boiling water hits the grounds it is aromatic for an instant, its smell better than its bitter, penitential taste. Lars gives it precisely four minutes to brew. This small chunk of defined time is a comfort. It's the only occasion that he ever looks at the watch suspended from a tin mirror on the cabin wall. On Halvmaneoya time and space are threads slipping from him. Yesterday he calculated the number of bears he has killed, or in whose death he has had a hand. He can recall the total for each season. He can almost distinguish each kill, but not quite, there are some which elude him. There will be a ban in place before next winter, there has to be. He knows polar bears better than any other living thing. For a decade he has trapped and gutted and skinned them, without ever understanding that they were flesh and blood; begotten, just as his daughter was. When he killed his first bear he made carvings from its bones. He whittled in the circle of light from his lamp. Bone after bone. He made bears standing upright, with eyes, noses and ears, but often with no mouth. The first were rudimentary and his lack of skill frustrated him. But he learnt to be patient. He learnt to understand the material he was using and to forget himself. And then they began to arrive. In his dreams, through his fingers. Bear after bear. He took the first one he carved back for Marta. 'I don't like it. It looks blind and it reminds me that you kill bears. Take it away again, it doesn't belong here.' She was lying in the hammock on the porch. With a yawn she rolled over and closed her eyes, letting her arms dangle over the edge, her fingers trailing lightly on the dusty tiles.

The next season he carved thirty more. Every moment that he wasn't trapping or skinning or sleeping he was whittling.

'Reparation,' Sivertsen told him. 'Replacement bears.'

'What do you mean?'

'I mean that you're honouring your dead. You're in communion with the bears' souls.'

'Souls?'

'Yes.'

His daughter is buried in the municipal cemetery at the edge of town. The undertaker made no charge for her funeral. Marta visits the grave four times a year. Lars has never been. Last winter he carved a baby in a foetal position. A tiny rosebud of a child carved into a bear's hip joint. He won't take the carvings back, they will stay here, with the dead, where they belong.

He wakes with a jolt; in his temples, the pulse of the Arctic is unfurling its deep, circadian rhythm, beat by beat. He has been asleep, drifting for about six hours he reckons. He knows immediately that the storm has changed direction, and sits up, craning to hear. He concentrates, trying to distinguish between the blood in his veins and the noise out there, in the night. He had been dreaming of the Sunday craft market in Oslo where Marta sells her quilts. She goes there once a month, and when he's home he goes with her. He helps her to load and unload the car. Marta greets the other stallholders like long lost friends and they complain about the poor weather. They stay over in a warehouse commune run by students, and in his dream Lars was trying to explain to Marta how, when he wakes in the night, he catches the whisper of Svalbard deep in his cells. 'Cabin fever,' Marta had laughed, flicking him playfully on the shoulder and stretching out on the makeshift bed with a comfortable sigh.

Lars hauls himself out of his bunk. The wind is beginning to clear, shifting to the south. Minute by minute he can hear the gale receding and the vast polar silence re-asserting itself. Out of the mass of shadow, shapes begin to distinguish themselves. He picks up his bearskin jacket and boots from beside the stove. Grief has been running like a fever in his body for weeks, making him weary, and it is an effort to get his outdoor clothes on, but he needs to stand outside under the suddenly calm reaches of Arctic sky. Pushing the cabin door open against the snow, Lars scans the uninterrupted lines of the landscape as far as he can see. There's no reflected star or moonlight but he is attuned to the tonal quality of the snowfields. Stepping out he watches where the storm is moving away. He knows that next season Halvmaneoya will be lost to him, that his island of bones will be picked clean by frost and empty air. Ice and blood and loneliness are the only certainties of his life here, but on this island she has followed him, the daughter he never knew. On Halvmaneoya she is the wind and she is the snow, she is the turning of each seamless midnight. She is the shooting star that trails its bright intensity across the arc of darkness, and next winter when the storms bring her, he won't be here. Lars doesn't know if he can bear it. On Halvmaneoya she has always travelled with him, tucked under his heart, but looking up through tears he sees the aurora flickering green and purple above the horizon, and Lars knows that it is taking her away from him. She is drifting away, his Winter-Child, his beloved. She is drifting away, beautiful, unearthly, southwards across the Svalbard Sea.

WILLIAM KONARZEWSKI

Pig Swill

The police say I murdered Brian Lavender. Whilst I take some responsibility for his death, I did not murder him. It was the O'Sullivans who murdered him, although of course I couldn't tell the police that. You never said anything bad about the O'Sullivans to the police unless you were tired of living. To be honest, I quite liked Brian, once I'd got used to him. There were flaws in his character. But if it were up to me, he'd still be alive.

I first met Brian Lavender on the day the O'Sullivans got him out of prison. He was doing life for stoving in someone's skull with a three foot length of scaffolding pole. They reckon he might have got away with it if he hadn't kept the murder weapon as a souvenir and stashed it under his bed.

There were six of us waiting for him at a safe house – a farm in Essex near Chelmsford. We were going to be his minders. I'd never been a minder before and I didn't want to be one. And if I had wanted to be one, I wouldn't have picked Brian as my first client. My ambition was to run the O'Sullivans' fruit machines. That was worth five hundred a week, along with a flat over a pub, and a minder to take care of me when I was collecting cash. Best of all it was legitimate – as legitimate as anything could be where the O'Sullivans were involved.

Patrick O'Sullivan spoke to me on the day before they broke Brian out of jail. We were in a car outside the Brick and Tile in Deptford. Patrick was a large man in a dark suit with an open neck shirt. He had red hair that was just starting to go grey. A jagged scar creased one of his cheeks. He wore a chunky gold ring on each finger of his right hand. They weren't purely decorative.

'I'm flattered you chose me,' I said after he'd told me what he wanted of me. 'But there's better guys than me for this job.'

Patrick just smiled. 'You'll be fine,' he said in his Irish accent. 'Just do what Kevin tells you. You're only there to make up the numbers.'

He seemed in a good mood and there was beer on his breath so I tried my luck again. 'I'd be more use to you on the fruit machines.'

'Well, it's strange you should say that,' he said with a grin, 'because I'm thinking about it. You do a good job with Mr Lavender and I'll think about it some more.'

Fortunately, the other five lads were hefty blokes who looked useful. There was Kevin, who was in charge, Spider, who had one tattooed on his neck, Cokey, Nose and Clem. Clem was half Trinidad, half Jamaica. Kevin called him mixed race which everyone thought was hilarious. I laughed out of politeness. It made sense to be good buddies with Kevin. If Clem minded, he didn't show it.

We were crowded around the TV. Brian's escape was the only item on the news, along with regular warnings not to approach him as he was dangerous. A slight understatement if you ask me. He'd also been in prison for removing half of someone's face with a cutthroat razor. And whilst inside, he'd regularly assaulted the warders and other prisoners. Outside, we could hear police sirens going up and down the main roads, and at frequent intervals there was the clatter-chatter of a chopper flying overhead.

Although I was apprehensive about meeting Brian, I was also excited. Sad really. But it was the first time I was going to get close to a real celebrity.

'You gotta respect a guy like that,' said Cokey.

There was a general murmur of assent.

'Yeah. I wouldn't wanna piss him off,' said Nose. It was obvious why they called him that. His snout wouldn't have looked out of place on Concord.

Spider glanced at his watch. 'Getting late,' he said. 'Plod might have picked him up.'

'Nah,' said Kevin, lighting up a cigarette and nodding at the TV. 'We'd have heard by now if they had.'

There was a silence. 'Anyone know why Patrick's getting him out of jail?' I asked.

Everyone looked at each other open mouthed as if I'd asked about the meaning of life.

'Maybe he's got a job for him,' said Spider at length.

Kevin shrugged. 'I reckon he just owes him.'

I nodded. It didn't really matter why Patrick wanted him out of jail. Our job was to look after him until the heat died down. After that he wasn't our problem.

It was going dark when some men arrived in a big white van and ushered Brian into the kitchen.

One of the escorts had shaggy, dirt-brown hair that hung down to his shoulders. He stank of stale tobacco and wore a donkey jacket.

'He's got to stay in the house, right,' he said in an Irish accent. 'Out of sight until the hunt dies down.'

'Sure. Patrick told us,' said Kevin. 'Don't worry. We'll take good care of him.'

The men vanished, saying they had to burn the van and get back to London.

We introduced ourselves to Brian who acknowledged everyone with a vacant nod until it got to me.

'Hi, I'm Alec,' I said.

Brian looked me up and down. 'Hello Smart Alec,' he said speaking slowly in a deep voice. 'So you're the one with the brains.'

I didn't know what to say. He might have been making fun of me. So I just smiled.

Brian Lavender was six foot four and weighed around seventeen stone of solid beef and bone. He had dense, black, curly hair. His forehead was narrow but he compensated by having plenty of space between his eyes.

'I'll have my dinner now,' he said, like we were hotel staff.

We had half a dozen Chinese take-away meals in tin foil containers in the oven. Brian ate the lot whilst watching TV with fixed frown. He didn't say much although he livened up whenever his picture came on and said, 'That's me. That's why I've got to stay inside the house. Right Smart Alec?'

I'd nod. 'That's right, Brian.'

'I'm Public Enemy Number One.'

'That's right, Brian.'

When he'd eaten, we gave him some cans of lager and had a few ourselves.

Suddenly he turned away from the news. 'Have you got any DVDs?' he asked. 'Tom and Jerry?'

I put on Tom and Jerry. He laughed, making a gurgling noise like a dishwasher at the end of its cycle.

Several DVDs later, he went to bed. But not before thanking me personally as if I were the only one who'd done anything for him. 'Good night, Smart Alec.'

'He likes you,' said Spider. 'You want to be careful. I've heard he likes fit young boys. Got the taste in prison.'

'Yeah, yeah,' I said, knowing he was only trying to wind me up. But the same thought had occurred to me. I decided to keep my distance from Brian.

For the first few hours of the next day, Brian was happy to stay inside the house. I'd managed to convince him there were thousands of police combing the area for him. The DVDs kept him occupied and I cooked sausages, bacon and eggs for him whenever he asked, which was soon after he'd finished the previous batch.

By the afternoon, though, he got restless.

'This is a farm, isn't it?' he said. 'I want to feed the animals.'

'They don't need feeding,' said Kevin. 'There's workers doing that.'

I took him upstairs to look out of a window. The farmhouse was a good distance from the farmyard with the dairy and piggery and henhouse. But we were close enough to see some guys dressed up in dungarees and check shirts wandering around as if they were auditioning for *Oklahoma*.

'We don't want them to see you,' I explained.

'I got you Smart Alec,' said Brian. 'Maybe I'll have a shufti when they've gone home.'

A police siren wailed outside. Good timing, I thought.

The sound plainly registered with Brian. 'You're the one with the brains, Smart Alec,' he said. I believed he meant it this time, but it wasn't that great a compliment. Only two of the other five could read the *Sun* without mouthing the words. Spider and Cokey just looked at the pictures.

Anyway, I used my brain to invent a new way of keeping Brian occupied. There was an indoor pool, fifteen metres long. In my wisdom, I suggested to him that he might enjoy a swim.

'I can't swim,' he said.

'I'll teach you,' I said without thinking it through.

There was a long silence. I was fearful I'd upset him and started slowly backing away. He had a reputation for fits of unexpected and irrational rage.

'Yeah, why not?' he said. A big grin split his face. 'I'd like that.'

I relaxed.

Leroy and Nose went out and returned with some swimming gear. They'd chosen bright yellow surfing pants which came down below the knee and had sharks printed on them.

Brian couldn't wait to get them on.

'Sharks,' he said. 'They'll kill anything.'

I winked at Leroy and Nose and they winked back at me.

The first swimming lesson went well until Brian decided to get playful. He clamped a large paw round the back of my neck and held me under. I threshed around in a desperate attempt to surface but he didn't let go. I don't remember too much after that until I came around gasping and spluttering on the side of the pool.

Brian was patting my cheeks. His forehead was furrowed and his eyes were locked on to mine. 'I'm sorry, Smart Alec,' he said. 'I thought you was enjoying it.'

'I was until my lungs filled with water,' I said, feeling like one of Lenny's mice in *Of Mice and Men*.

'I want to go to McDonalds,' he said later.

'We can get you a take-away,' I said.

'No, I want to eat in the restaurant.'

'Not safe. You'll be recognised.'

'I could wear dark glasses and a baseball cap.'

'They'll still recognise you. You're a head taller than everyone else.'

This made Brian go silent. 'Yeah. You're right,' he said after some moments. 'You're the one with the brains, Smart Alec.'

'Why don't we play cards whilst someone gets you some burgers and fries?'

Brian smiled.

We played snap. I let him win. This wasn't purely out of sportsmanship. When Brian brought the flat of his hand down on the table, you didn't want your hand underneath it. After that we moved on to snakes and ladders. He wasn't the fastest player in Essex. I had to explain what he needed to do with every throw of the dice. It was hard work. But there was something satisfying about managing him. I doubted if any of the other lads could do that. They just watched us and said stupid things in the background.

After an hour, this began to get on my wick and I said: 'Give us a break, boys.'

One of them laughed.

Brian rose to his feet, scraping his chair noisily on the stone floor. He picked an apple out of the fruit bowl on the table and squeezed it. Juice and pulp emerged from between his fingers.

After displaying his novel technique for making cider, he spoke: 'He said shut up. He can't concentrate with all your noise.' His voice was flat and deep and there was no expression on his face. But you could have heard an ant sneeze. The boys vacated the room as if they'd seen a time-bomb with three seconds left on the clock.

For a week I struggled to find ways of keeping Brian happy and indoors. The other lads devoted themselves to playing poker, smoking and drinking lager. Eventually I had an idea that was so beautiful and so obvious I couldn't imagine why I hadn't thought of it before. What Brian needed was a girl.

The O'Sullivans sent Sharon down from London. She was blonde and pretty with pert little breasts. I quite fancied her myself. I don't know what they paid her, but she was worth it. She kept Brian occupied in his room for hours and spent the night.

'The bitch will make us redundant,' said Leroy.

I wasn't so sure.

In the morning, Sharon had to leave.

'I gotta go now,' she said to Brian after having a cup of tea with him at the kitchen table.

'I don't want you to go,' said Brian taking hold of her hand.

'My nan needs me,' said Sharon. 'She's proper poorly and she ain't got no one else. I have to bandage her legs and do her shopping and all that.' She lied as naturally as I guessed she did everything else.

'When are you coming back?'

'Tomorrer.'

Brian nodded. 'Promise.'

She showed all her teeth in a sparkling smile. 'Yeah. 'Course I promise. Can't wait to see you again. You make me feel like a real woman.'

Brian released her hand and grinned as if the Home Secretary had just given him a free pardon.

Sharon returned the next day, and two days after that.

'I'm in love with her, Smart Alec,' Brian he said to me after their third meeting. 'I'm going to marry her.'

'That's good, Brian,' I said. 'Congratulations.'

'And you're coming to the wedding, Smart Alec,' he said.

'Wow, that's great. Thanks mate,' I said.

'You're going to be my best man,' he said. 'I don't care what anyone says.'

I think he assumed Patrick O'Sullivan might have wanted to be best man.

On the morning after Sharon's fourth visit, Brian came to me, shaking and sweating.

'I want you to look at Sharon,' he said, gulping in air between each word.

I knew what I was going to find, but it didn't make it any easier. She was stark naked and had purple bruises all over her neck, the size of fingerprints. There was an obscene angle between her head and her torso. Her lips were blue and she had blood in her nostrils.

'Is she all right?' he asked. 'Do you think she wants an ambulance?'

'She's going to be fine,' I said. 'But she needs a special doctor. Why don't you go down to the pool and keep out of sight?'

'Are you sure she'll be all right?' he asked.

'Sure I'm sure, big fellow,' I said. 'Now the sooner you go to the pool, the sooner we can get her sorted.'

'Thanks, Smart Alec. She said she wasn't going to marry me.'

I nodded. 'She'll be fine... good as new.'

Now some folk might have been more honest with Brian, but I'd just seen what had happened to Sharon when she'd said something he didn't want to hear.

Kevin telephoned Patrick O'Sullivan with the news.

I stood near enough to hear the conversation. Patrick O'Sullivan never whispered anything that could equally well be bellowed from the rooftops.

'Jaysus, feckin lunatic,' said Patrick. He paused briefly. 'Chop her up and feed her to the pigs. Then clean up proper like. Burn her clothes and bag. Anything that doesn't burn, bury it. A long way away. We don't want no traces.'

'What about Brian?' Kevin asked.

'Leave him to me,' said Patrick. 'We're going to have to move him fast. Don't let him out of the house. Shoot him if you have to.'

'Sure, boss,' said Kevin.

'And get the workers off the farm. Give them money. Tell them it's a family party and I want total privacy.'

'Sure boss.'

There was click at the other end of the line.

Kevin turned to me. 'Watch him. Keep him in the pool. Use this if you have to.' He produced a revolver from a biscuit tin in one of the cupboards. I stuck it in my pocket. It was the first time I'd handled a gun, but I wasn't going to admit it. Anyway, I reckoned it wasn't necessary to have a diploma in ballistics to point and pull a trigger. You get a lesson in almost every film you see.

Kevin snapped some orders to the boys before going outside and heading towards the bit parts in *Oklahoma*.

Spider and Nose helped themselves to a meat cleaver and large knife from the kitchen utensils, whilst Leroy and Cokey went upstairs to fetch Sharon.

'Where you taking her?' asked Brian appearing on the scene as they lugged her limp body through the kitchen. He fixed a pair of wide staring eyes on her body.

Thankfully he didn't notice what Spider and Nose were holding. Neither did he notice Cokey's hand moving slowly towards the sleek swelling in his trouser pocket.

'Outside,' I said hastily. 'We don't want the doctor coming in the house.'

Brian gazed down at Sharon. I heard the kitchen clock tick off five seconds. 'Good as new you say, Smart Alec?'

'You'd never know anything happened to her,' I said. 'Why don't we go down to the pool?"

I took him down to the pool. He came with me, docile as a child. Before long he was on the diving board in his yellow surfing shorts. He seemed to have forgotten about Sharon. Or else he really thought she'd do a Lazarus.

'Come in,' he shouted, giving me a hearty splash that drenched the wall behind me.

'Can't,' I said, wiping water out of my eyes. 'Got to be ready for the doctor.'

'Is that who Kevin was speaking to on the 'phone?'

'Yes.'

He gazed at me for a few seconds. You couldn't tell if he believed you or was planning to kill you. There was never a dull moment with Brian. I was relieved when he clambered out of the pool and mounted the diving board.

Whilst he plunged repeatedly into the water, I started working out what was going to happen next. You didn't need to be Einstein to do that. Patrick was going to kill him. It was going to be a waste of all the effort – and expense – of getting him out of jail. But the man was a mad dog, and Patrick O'Sullivan wasn't sentimental when it came to cutting his losses.

Now I'm no Mother Teresa, and I didn't want to miss out on the fruit machines by getting Patrick O'Sullivan narked. But I didn't want Brian's blood on my hands. There was a part of me that had got attached to the man. God knows why, he'd nearly drowned me and what he'd done to Sharon wasn't nice. I reckoned the only thing to do was to let him escape and hope the police caught him before the O'Sullivans did.

'You need to get the hell out of here, Brian,' I said, when he came up to stand near me dripping wet. His mouth was hanging open as if he expected me to dream up some new game for him.

'I like it here,' he said.

'Just get out of here, Brian. Listen to me, for God's sake.'

He frowned. 'What's wrong Smart Alec?'

'Just wait here,' I said. 'Don't move. I've got something for you.'

He looked like a kid waiting for Father Christmas.

I went up to my room and returned as quickly as I could.

'Here's some money.' I gave him a hundred pounds in twenties and a piece of paper with an address. 'Get a taxi or a train and go back to London. You're safe there.'

'But I thought...'

'No one's going to recognise you Brian. Everyone's forgotten about your escape. It's old news. Yesterday's papers.'

His big mouth sagged. 'I don't understand.'

'Patrick's coming to kill you.'

'Is it because of Sharon?'

'I don't know.'

'I want a gun.'

His eyes were fixed on my pocket and I guessed he knew I wasn't that pleased to see him. I gave him the gun. Yes, I should have shot him there and then. It would have saved me and everyone else a lot of bother, and

I'd have been the O'Sullivans' blue-eyed boy for a while. They'd have given me anything I asked for. But even if I'd wanted to, I hadn't got the guts. If I missed, Brian would eat me alive, never mind joining Sharon inside the pigs.

'You're all right Smart Alec,' he said, taking the gun and flipping open the cylinder to check it was loaded.

I forced a smile and ushered him to his clothes where I helped him dry himself.

When he was dressed, he went outside. I heaved a sigh of relief. I reckoned the police would pick him pretty quickly. It didn't take long to realise I'd underestimated Brian's stupidity. He headed at once for the piggery. He was going to take a look at the pigs before leaving. When he saw the boys chopping up his beloved Sharon, he wasn't going to believe it was life-saving surgery.

I ran after him. 'No Brian, not that way.'

But I was too late.

The boys were coming back from the piggery. Brian must have thought they were coming to say goodbye because he stopped and waved at them in a friendly way. They pulled out guns and started shooting. Something zinged past my ear and I flung myself on the ground. Brian staggered backwards. God knows how, he managed to get out my gun and shoot back. The boys didn't give him time to take proper aim. They carried on shooting until he stopped moving. Twelve, maybe fifteen shots. Kevin walked up and put final bullet in his head at point black range. I can't say I blamed him. You don't take any chances with a man like Brian. Not if you've seen any films about cyborgs.

'You all right?' Kevin asked me, helping me to get up.

'Yeah, I'm f-fine,' I stammered. 'He took the gun off me. I couldn't stop him.'

Kevin nodded. 'No harm done.'

I stared down at Brian's blood spattered carcass. He could have been a body double for Clyde Barrow at the end of *Bonnie and Clyde*. 'No harm done,' I said.

Two of the farm workers came up and gawped. It seemed they hadn't got the message about going for an early lunch. They had bug eyes like emoticons that have sat on broken bottles.

'Go home,' said Kevin. 'You didn't see nothing. You didn't hear nothing. Mr O'Sullivan will sort you out later. Make it worth your while.'

'Is that who I think it is?' asked one of the workers in a slow deep voice that might have belonged to Brian.

'Yes. Now bugger off.'

The lad stared for a while at the smoking gun in Kevin's hand before shuffling away with his mate.

'You didn't see nothing, you didn't hear nothing, you don't know nothing,' Kevin shouted after them.

'Got yer, mate,' said the other worker, turning and giving a thumb's up.

Functioning on automatic pilot, I went over to the body and picked up my gun and put it in my pocket with a trembling hand. The boys dragged Brian's body off to the piggery except for Kevin who walked towards the house. I went with Kevin.

'You think they'll keep their mouths shut?' I asked, pointing after the disappearing labourers.

'Patrick will sort them out,' said Kevin. 'I'd better let him know what's happened.'

In the house, Kevin called Patrick O'Sullivan. Kevin held the receiver a distance from his face as he weathered the early storm of abuse.

Eventually Patrick became coherent. 'Jaysus, why didn't you feckin eejits just take him outside feckin Chelmsford police station with feckin drums and pipes and feckin shoot him there with a feckin AK47?'

'I'm sorry, Patrick,' said Kevin. 'He just went out of control. It happened too quick for us.'

'He did have a hasty temper on him, to be sure,' said Patrick, sounding calmer. 'Now clean up the place and get back to London. Wipe everything Brian's touched. I'll send Dermot down to speak to the farm boys.'

Brian was one of those people who go around touching everything like a kid in a toyshop. Whilst Spider and Clem made sure the pigs finished their breakfast, the rest of us ran round with baby wipes going over the surfaces and windows.

We were making good progress when the police turned up. Five cars with blue lights, barking dogs the size of Shetland ponies and a couple of black riot vans. A chopper rattled in the sky above. The cops piled out of their cars right away, dressed in helmets and body armour. They bristled with Glocks and carbines. It's the kind of scene I like better on TV than in real life.

'Police. Come outside with your hands in the air,' said a voice on a loudspeaker.

We just about had time to wipe our guns and put them in toilet cisterns before going outside.

'Now listen carefully,' said Roger Hamilton my QC. He was a thin man, with thin grey hair, thin lips and a long thin nose which supported a pair of rimless glasses. His suit was the sort of suit you don't often see outside weddings. He had a slimline stainless steel brief case with a combination lock.

We were sitting in a room in Chelmsford Police Station. It had bars inside the windows and peeling yellow paint on the walls.

'I'm listening,' I said.

He continued. 'I think you and your colleagues were staying at the farm for a holiday when some men you'd never seen before turned up in a white van and dumped Brian Lavender on you. They gave you guns and told you to look after him. After that they went away. You can't remember the number of the van. Brian went wild a few days later and attacked you with a kitchen knife so you shot him.'

He paused and stared into my eyes as if to check this wasn't too complicated for me.

I nodded. 'Got you. Self-defence. Then what?'

Hamilton continued. 'The men turned up and took the body away. They said something about dumping it in the sea off Harwich.'

'And everyone's going to believe me?'

He removed his rimless glasses and polished the thin lenses with a pristine white handkerchief. 'You're a villain. No one's going to believe a word you say even if it's all on CCTV.' He replaced his glasses and gave me an icy smile.

'So I get two years with a year off for good conduct?'

'As long as your behaviour is immaculate.'

'Don't I get off with nothing if it's self-defence?'

He shook his head. 'You'll be charged with firearms offences.'

I nodded. I'd forgotten about the guns. 'What about Sharon?'

'In terms of this case, Sharon never existed. I know nothing about her. No one else knows anything about her. You don't need to mention her.'

I nodded again. I thought of her pert little breasts and the way she winked at me on her way up to Brian's room. She was only about twenty and she'd have been alive if I hadn't had that stupid idea about getting a girl for Brian.

'Collateral damage,' I said.

Hamilton stared right through me.

'And you don't need to mention anyone else either,' he said. 'Keep it simple. Stick to the facts.'

It was his way of saying I wasn't to squeal on the O'Sullivans. Of course he couldn't actually say that out loud. It wouldn't have been professional.

'Got you,' I said.

He got up to leave.

'One thing,' I said.

He looked at me with raised eyebrows.

'When I come out, I'm going straight,' I said.

'I'm glad to hear that,' he said in a dry voice. 'What are you planning to do?'

'Fruit machines,' I said. 'I want you to pass that on.'

He didn't say anything. His face remained blank. He snapped his briefcase shut, twirled the combination lock and stood up.

I served a year. Kevin, Spider, Clem, Cokey and Nose also got a year. The police asked me a lot of questions about the O'Sullivans and said I didn't need to go to jail if I told them what they wanted to know. You can always tell when the police are lying. Their lips move. I didn't tell them anything.

The others didn't tell them anything either. I know that because they're alive and still have a full quota of teeth and fingers. Cokey's only got one large nostril, but that's not down to the O'Sullivans.

When I got out of Wandsworth, Patrick O'Sullivan sent a car for me.

'I've been thinking,' he said over a pint at the Brick and Tile, 'a smart boy like you could use a break. I've got some fruit machines that need looking after. What do you say son?'

We shook hands on the deal and he bought me another pint. And another.

'I'd like to ask you something,' I said after the third pint.

The scar on his cheek puckered into a grisly smile. 'Go on.'

'Why did you spring Brian, if you don't mind my asking?'

'Jaysus,' he said. 'It's the biggest feckin mistake I ever made. But I'll tell you something. He was a lovely feller. Man after me own heart.'

ANNIE MACCONNEL

Kwality

Alice watches the golfers thirty-seven floors below. This is at the window bank in the southwest corner of the Communications Department where Claudine Paul is dropping candy hearts wrapped in red, white, and blue cellophane on everyone's desk. She doles out candy hearts for each holiday and this is her Fourth of July offering. 'No problem!' Claudine repeats again and again in response to every thank you, making her way through the stable of cubicles. Alice waits for some variation, just one 'you're welcome' or 'my pleasure.' Nola, in the cube across from Alice, covers the gift with her hand. 'So shines a good deed in a weary world,' she says. Then she tosses the package into a drawer. She'll find it months from now, the hearts crushed and powdery.

Alice fantasizes about joining them, outside in the free world, though she's never golfed. It's an accounting firm not a prison, she could leave anytime. Except that her rent is due Friday and will continue to be due as long as the earth travels around the sun with her on board.

'No problem!' says Claudine. Alice is vaguely worried about her. There's ample time here for vague worry.

'Lady's a damn cyborg,' mumbles Davis from the mailroom, pushing his cart.

* * *

YUM YUM. URA TIGER. Alice lines up the best of the hearts on Nola's desk and eats the rest. 'A quality snack,' she says. DDBA is campaigning to win a prestigious National Quality Award and she's begun to hear the word in her dreams. She sees it floating before her, Quality, and now it has no meaning. She puts together graphics presentations: *What is Quality to DDBA*? The answers are examined in neat bullet points. She distributes colorful paper flyers throughout the office: *Quality is You, DDBA's Employees*. The flyers list, with a grateful tone, the ways DDBA's employees work hard to produce so much quality. She recognizes it for what it is: a desperate buttering-up meant to prepare employees for the

Quality People from National Quality Headquarters who are soon coming to interview random workers about the ways DDBA does or does not possess Quality.

She receives key chains and magnets and plastic credit card holders that say *DDBA Quality*.

Near the State and Lake 'L' station, where she enters and leaves downtown Chicago every weekday, is an Indian restaurant named Kwality.

'We put the K in quality,' Nola likes to say.

* * *

Nola pins a Vermeer postcard from the Art Institute on the tack board wall of her cubicle. The night before, they brought Nola's fourteen-year-old son, Owen, to an exhibit. 'The genius is in the light,' Alice had said. 'How can you do that with paint? It doesn't seem possible.' Owen had put his hands in his pockets and scanned for the exit. 'I don't know,' he'd said. 'It's good, I guess.'

When Alice was a few years older than Owen she'd kept a list. Bathrobes, student council, *Better Homes and Gardens*, camping, dental appointments, etc. She called it 'Normal Things' and her criteria couldn't be explained, she just knew if something belonged or didn't. Maps belonged, diaries didn't. Diaries could be useful and also interesting, but they were not, strictly speaking, normal. Many interesting things weren't. Eventually the list embarrassed her, but at the height of her pursuit she saw every entry as a brick, one on top of another, slowly building a solid and protective structure she hoped to someday occupy.

* * *

When she returns to her cube, Alice's phone rings.

'Are you gonna jump?' It's Nola.

'Excuse me?'

'Out the window.'

'I might. People are down there, just sailing on Lake Michigan and golfing at ten o'clock on a Wednesday morning.'

'Heirs and heiresses, I guess.'

'Is "heiress" offensive now, like "poetess"? Maybe it's "heirs" for all of them.'

April Dubanowski teeters down the aisle in three-inch heels, carrying a small nylon bag tucked under her arm. The bag holds her curling iron. She curls her hair twice in the bathroom each day, before her lunch break and an hour before leaving. Craig Molek trails April Dubanowski on his way back from the break room, holding two Mountain Dews, one in each hand. He'll get two more in the afternoon. His Mountain Dew schedule and April's hair schedule correspond. Alice hears the metal of his swivel chair settling beneath him and then the pop of the can.

'Everything's in order,' Nola says.

'No problem!' sings Claudine Paul, a dozen or so cubicle rows away.

* * *

They have a fifty-minute lunch break. Alice eats microwaved mac and cheese and a red, white, and blue supermarket cupcake, courtesy of Building Services, in the break room. She opens an abandoned Life section from *USA Today* and reads about a famous American actor vacationing with friends at his lakeside villa in northern Italy.

At one o'clock she takes the elevator to thirty-eight for her biannual employee review. The new manager, Rollie Lamb, has been at DDBA two months. He is always sunburned and subtly perfumed and quietly amused by his own private thoughts. He generally behaves as though attending a dreaded family reunion, chatting in a politely stingy manner while scanning the room for someone who might produce a gin and tonic.

'Hello, Allison!' Rollie Lamb is standing at his brown, wooden, hunk of a desk.

'Alice.'

He picks up her file. 'Alice! My apologies. Everyone around here is Allison! I've had two of them already today.'

She sits in the small, upholstered chair across from him.

'Two reviews, I mean.'

Propped on his desk is a framed photo. An elderly yellow Labrador lounging on vast, green lawn.

'Goldie. My ex-wife would've taken him, too, but he sheds and he smells bad.' Rollie sits and slaps his thighs. 'Alice! Tell me about your goals here.'

'I'd like to attend some of the career development seminars at the Schaumburg campus.' She has rehearsed this. 'Ideally I want to be managing new projects, down the road.' How is it that Alice has ended up here, in Rollie Lamb's office, saying these words? She has no interest in managing projects or attending seminars in Schaumburg.

'Let me tell you something, Alice. My dear mother, Elizabeth Lamb, died of an aneurysm on the eve of her thirty-ninth birthday. Wonderful, beautiful woman. *Fwoot*. Gone.'

'I'm sorry.'

'No, no, don't be sorry. That's not why we're here. This is about you and your goals. Alice, think about what lights you up in this world. What lights you up?'

For this she has no rehearsed answer.

'Listen, Alice. I saw *The Matrix* over the weekend. Caught it on cable. Have you seen it? Basically, this guy has always believed there was something wrong with the world and it turns out he's right. It's a movie that makes you think. But that's neither here nor there. Socrates said, "The secret of happiness is not found in seeking more, but in developing the capacity to enjoy less." ' This is punctuated with an explosive laugh. Then Rollie glances at Alice's file and thumbs through its pages.

'Alice, it looks to me like you're doing a fine job here. I see you received a two percent raise in December. Wonderful! Any questions, Alice?'

'I don't think so, no.'

'Very good, Alice. Great work. Enjoy the holiday weekend!'

* * *

Her phone rings.

'You left something in Rollie Lamb's office.' It's Nola again.

'I did?' Alice turns and looks at her. She's facing the wall of her cube.

'Your soul.'

* * *

Andrina from Ken's office calls. Ken, a senior accountant on twenty-four, needs his report. Alice clips it with a Report Binder, slides it into a Report Folder and exits the Communications Department toward the elevator bank.

This is when she sees R.

He's standing alone, staring straight ahead at the closed elevator doors. She has never spoken to him. She knows his name only because he used to wear a plastic nametag pinned to his shirt.

R, a fortyish, paunchy, pockmarked employee from the Copy Center, is wearing mascara and a printed cotton skirt instead of his usual button-down and khaki pants. His drab hair is curled and sprayed and he – she – clearly has breasts beneath her cardigan sweater. She – R – waits earnestly for the bell to ding and the doors to open, clutching a stack of booklets (*Quality, Growth, and Global Impact*) in one hand, and a lavender handbag in the other.

Alice would be lying if she said this isn't thrilling. If she said this doesn't seem like a gift. It isn't voyeuristic curiosity – she knows what that feels like. It's pure joy, witnessing R thoroughly transformed within the regulated universe of DDBA.

She approaches cautiously, not wanting to burden R with the intensity of her admiration. R is of course simply attending to the necessary business of being R; she'd likely prefer that this, her mere presence, not be a spectacle for others. But Alice can't deny it. She finds her mere presence spectacular and is moved to say something.

She wants it to be the right thing. Something that might crack R open and break her fixed gaze, make her look at Alice square in the eye and smile with recognition, smile in a way that's real and unforced. Something that might make her want to grab Alice's arm, push the 'lobby' button in the elevator and descend all thirty-seven floors, past the Copy Center, past Ken the senior accountant on twenty-four, past the supermarket baked goods, the industrial carpeting, the controlled climate, and out together into the shimmering world.

Alice can only think to compliment R's skirt, but the comment seems to offend her. She doesn't reply and they ride the elevator together in silence.

Ken on twenty-four gets his report, April Dubanowski curls her hair, Craig Molek drinks his Mountain Dews and at five o'clock they are free to go.

WENDY RILEY

Amir's Story

There was a cat up in the mountains, grandad said, who smiled all over her face. Not just from the side, as most cats do, but from every angle you could find. Goodness knows why, grandad said, because everyone took a pot-shot at that animal. The Russians wanted to make hats out of her pelt. The Mujahideen tried to bet on her in cat fights. The Taliban decided to exterminate her as vermin. But no-one could catch her, she was a devil of a runner; she slipped into clouds and shadows to save her ginger skin. You could say there was a price on this cat's head, but she never stopped smiling. I wish I had known this cat. She was just like me. I, too, grinned when I should have been wailing, and laughed in the face of horrors. Much to the shame of my parents, of course, who lived in a permanent state of apology. Only grandad understood; he saw it as a natural state of affairs in a country so ravaged by war and riven with contradictions.

'But come on, my children, what do you expect?' he asked my mother and father when I had chuckled my way through the funeral of a small friend, Omar, whose face was blown away when he stepped on a landmine.

'Life has turned on its head. We have sold the Spring. April used to mean the melting of the snow, blossom and fruits, picnics, sun-dazzle, new love . . . ah, those new loves! Now it ushers in the Fighting Season. Children playing in green meadows explode in pieces. We pray for the icy cold dark to come back and save us from this terrible game. Is this not ridiculous and tragic enough to laugh at, if crying does no good?'

He was good with words, my grandad. He would sit for long evenings in the cafe, bending people's ears. He had a lot to say about everything. Mother said he should be paid for some of his speeches, but father said: 'Don't encourage him, my wife! Already we never hear the last of it. Perhaps we should just make a recording, stick it on one of the cafe chairs, and no-one will ever know the difference.'

Father sounded cross, but I think he was just worried about his dad aggravating the Taliban. It wasn't hard to do. I did it all the time, throwing laughter as a flame-thrower hurls fire. It was the clothing I slipped on in the morning; the last, careless thing I bounced against the bedroom wall at night. The Taliban hated a lot of things. But the thing they hated most of all was laughter. Perhaps, when they heard it, they knew that the person had slipped beyond them into a place of joy or disdain they could not reach. And if the person was laughing directly at them, they had also moved beyond fear.

I remember noisy conversations in my house. I remember a chaos of clothes and books and bottles. But more than anything I remember the fear of my father and mother as their children, daily, broke their hearts. Grandad and I would eye each other over the breakfast table as Ghezaal and Adeela drew up their daily agendas.

'Taliban Baiting', father called it. 'As idiotic as Bear Baiting and five times as dangerous. '

My oldest sister, Ghezaal, was a beauty who refused to hide it, choosing to wear Western jeans, boots and t-shirts which she foraged from various Kabul markets. Her hair flowed freely around her face, shining in the sun and bouncing on the winds which keened in from the mountains in winter. Her wide, brown eyes invited every disaster that her war-torn country might choose to throw at it. When she walked me through Kabul's crowded streets, I saw men melt around her; gesturing American soldiers, grinning lads, stern businessmen, fathers and sons. She showed no fear, not even when an Imam threw a Quran into her face, and screamed 'Whore'!; nor when a group of soldiers followed her home with leers on their faces and guns in their pockets. She picked me up and carried me, kissed my nose, and ducked swiftly into the bird market, losing her stalkers in a maze of squawking partridges and doves. Our house rang out to the sounds of *Coldplay*; neighbours would frequently bang on the doors at night, sometimes leaving 'Cease and Desist' messages pinned to the front door. We danced together to her longed-for tunes, her body weaving and spinning in the dusty hallway, mother holding her hijab in sheer frustration, as my other sister, Adeela, brushed past with a 'Whatever' shrug and her boy clothes giving her an air of swagger.

Adeela, then, was alternatively known as Idris, her boy name. My excursions with Adeela were different again, for she was now *Bacha Posh*, one of Afghanistan's growing army of girls dressed as boys.

'And why not, my Amir?' She asked me one day. 'Why be a nothing person?' Her short, bobbed hair framed her sturdy face, on top of a sturdy body which suited a boy's life perfectly.

'I will not be raped. I will not be beaten. I will not be ordered to live a life of boredom and shame. I will fly kites and drink wine and make money and walk the streets and I will protect those who can't protect themselves.'

Adeela and Ghezaal approached the same doom from different angles, and respected each other's persona.

'You will be the death of us, the pair of you', mother scolded them frequently. While *Bacha Posh* had been her idea, she had not anticipated the zeal with which Adeela adopted it. Designed to allow Adeela many freedoms denied to her as a girl, Adeela had already outstripped her role, becoming more boy than her mum had bargained for. She stared people in the eye, pushed back her shoulders, lifted her chin and swaggered past Taliban men with her hands in her pockets.

When I came along, then, I was a huge relief to parents who had longed for a regular boy in order to meet society's norms. Relief wore off pretty quickly though. When I started giggling in the face of disaster and bawling my eyes out at happy events, they knew they were in for trouble.

'Have we done something to offend Allah?' was my mother's plaintive question.

'Maybe it's the drug money', was my father's remorseful response, thinking of the years spent farming poppies in Kandahar.

'Maybe we all need to go back to the mountains and tend goats', was my grandad's suggestion, 'and wait for all the hippies to come back again. Allah or no Allah; it's all the same to me. Everyone tells me what to believe, and how to believe it. My God is my God is my God, and he belongs to *me*. No-one else can poke a stick at him.'

I often wondered about this God, belonging so exclusively to my grandfather. Perhaps everyone just had their own God, and refused to share. Every single person I had known, in my short life, believed something quite different from all the others. No two Gods appeared remotely alike. The Taliban insisted on only one God, their God, but I felt nothing in the place where a God should be.

There is no God but God.

There is no love, but a hole where love should be; there is no life but an endless struggle. That is what I felt deep inside, like a hidden seed, a shameful secret. I loved my family fiercely, but a void was gaping, beyond their capacity to fill. Thoughts of Omar scraped me at night, like fingernails. My lost friend had screamed for two days and two nights in the hospital, before he died; the painkillers had run out; his parents couldn't even kiss the place where his face had been. So when my own father began to talk about the boat, it seemed natural to think that the boat might hold all our hopes, however leaky. That it would take us to a place which was Godless – mercifully so – where we could start again.

Grandad used to be a grape grower, owning a little network of vineyards half-way up the mountain road to Istalif where he grew the sweetest fruit you could find in Kabul's markets. That was his story anyway, and he stuck to it. He employed his own son – my father Faisal – as soon as he was old enough, and when my father married my mother, Laila, he invested in fig and fruit trees to add to the crop. Mother and father started their life together in a little shack at the back of the property, where they grew roses and geraniums in summer and built snowmen when the winter snows blew bitter drifts across their garden. They escaped the worst of the Soviet invasion, tucked away into the hillside, sheltered from battles blazing across the Shomali Plain below. Grandad appeased the soldiers with regular fruit rations, slapping them on the back with loud congratulations only to spit and whisper '*Spee Bachee*!' as they left. In 1996 Ghezaal was born, just in time for the Taliban to capture Kabul. In 1999 Adeela was born, just in time for the Taliban to destroy houses and vineyards up and down the Shomali Plain, including grandad's. Devastated and frightened, the family fled to Kandahar, where fortunes could apparently be made growing poppies for opium. Grandad, cut off from the beauty and safety of the mountains, and everything he had known, railed day and night against his immoral son. But he had run out of options, like everyone else. He had misplaced his dreams. He wanted to believe his son when Faisal insisted they would farm the poppies for money enough to start a business in Kabul, where they might escape persecution. And then they would leave. In the end they were stuck in the desert for seven years, reaching Kabul with a nest egg in 2006. Just in time for me to arrive in April, fighting fit for the Fighting Season, screaming the odds and wired to laugh in all the wrong places.

It was hard living in Kabul, when I could see the mountains yawning up on all sides, enticing me in. I dreamed of the snow leopards who leapt from peak to peak, pounding their huge, plate-like paws through the thick snow. My sisters read to me of howling grey wolves, and linx which slipped through the gullies of the Hindu Kush like feline liquid.

I wasn't long in this world before I demanded a cat of my own, my only foreseeable way of retaining sanity. I felt suffocated by the crowded alleyways, and throngs of people bustling and bumping from bazaar to mosque. I knew that we had had a different reality, and it had been decimated; that love, and laughter, and hope had bubbled through our family before the unthinkable squeezed in and blew it all away. I could still see remnants of these lost dreams smeared on the cracking flags of our Kabul home, among the squashed flies and grit dragged in from the tired alleys; I could catch its currents flowing on the tide of my parents' conversations, before ebbing into despair.

So I started bringing cats home. Big cats, small cats, mangy cats, sleek cats, regal cats, squawling cats and any cat I could manage to smuggle back with me. I was spoiled for choice. Feral and abandoned cats littered the city, living twilight lives under cover of tenements and darkness. Covered with gouge marks from frantic claws, I fought the good fight and arrived home dripping blood, with another lost moggy ambivalent about being saved. My mother repeatedly refused to feed them, shooing them away with dagger looks in my direction. Until the day Cola came to stay, placid in my arms, draped against my small body like a sleeping bunny. Something in those unblinking eyes cast a spell on my mother, who melted like oil in the sun. By the time father came home, Cola – the colour of the drink with splashed white face and paws – was curled blissfully into our old couch with a purr so loud you could hear it over Ghezaal's *Coldplay* records.

My poor father; he limped through a procession of dire jobs which lasted anything from six weeks to one day. He had wanted to start up his own business, but resisted spending his money. He had other things on his mind.

'But what are you going to *do*, Faisal?' my mother would plead, sick of living hand to mouth, and worrying about her wayward daughters out on Kabul's mean streets. 'Why do you commit to nothing?'

She was used to father waving her away, sticking his head inside a newspaper, or mumbling under his breath about lost opportunities. But the day he mentioned the boat she sat heavily on her chair and rocked backwards and forwards, moaning.

'Are you mad, my husband? Do you know what happens to people on those contraptions?'

'What happens is people get to Australia and everything changes', my father said. 'Don't believe the stories you hear about boats sinking left, right and centre. That's what Governments want you to think, so you won't make the journey.'

'Over my dead body', mother said flatly, and the show was over.

Until the day that Adeela was blown to bits by a suicide bomber, as she was carrying home flatbreads from the baker near Babur's Gardens. Ghezaal told me of the blood sprayed high against the walls, a carnage shielded from the white marble and water gardens beyond. My mother and father were never the same again.

On the day of the funeral, mother looked at father with dead eyes and said: 'We're going. Book the passage. This country has killed me. I have no use for it any more.'

'It was a time of life and colour,' grandad said, 'the old hippy days in the Hindu Kush. Nobody bothered too much, then, about the length of your beard. You could be a hairy galoot or bald as a coot, and it all went down the same way. Women got around and about, doing proper jobs, and there was always someone to buy the carpets, fill the guest houses and admire the views.'

He went all glassy-eyed when he wandered down memory lane; father used to poke him in the ribs and call him a sentimental fool. But grandad pulled stories out of the air, building, block by block, in my head as people and places so vivid I might have remembered them myself. Far from our dusty tenement in the back blocks of Kabul, soared mountains so high and lakes so deeply blue that they made your eyes ache if you looked too long; if you tried to feast on their beauty; like cramming too many mulberries into your mouth in one go, you ended up dizzy with flavours bursting all over your tongue.

It was a journey into the unknown. Crammed into the back of a jolting truck, we wound our way across the border with Pakistan, fellow travellers packed thigh to thigh in the chilly dark. I peeked out once, seeing only a terrifying drop into an icy void. Mother scolded me for my curiosity.

'*It is better not to know*', she insisted.

I could never agree, nor could my sister Ghezaal, her eyes bright and hard with purpose. We still believed that life might be able to deliver itself to us, with some semblance of generosity and justice. I mourned my grandad, unable to attempt this arduous trek. As our plane bumped down through the clouds to Jakarta, I fancied I saw his face in their crinkled edges, eyes screwed up in mock disbelief.

'Will grandad be joining us later?' I asked mother.

She looked at me, without replying. Obviously not. Grandad had better things to do than rattle around in trucks and boats and planes, before disembarking in a baking hot country riddled with crazy kangaroos. On the plane, Ghezaal showed me a picture book full of Australian animals, some who lived in their mother's pouches, and others who killed you.

'Just show him the koalas!' mother whispered, wanting to keep it cute. But cute had never cut it for me. And as we landed in Indonesia, where we would wait to join our boat, the crush of bodies and elements welcomed us to a new reality where cute had died long ago, and could not be revived.

We lived for almost a year in a small flat on the twentieth floor of a tower block in downtown Jakarta. Father found work where he could, but the rest of us were instructed to stay within the bounds of the apartment complex. We felt strangled by our shrunken life in a country we didn't understand.

Other families and young men came and went, staying with us briefly before disappearing in the middle of the night. Sometimes they came back, mortified and spent, having been turned back by police blocks; one young Iranian lad had already tried four times to reach Australia, once almost dying when his boat went down. Mother put her fingers in her ears when he related his story; this was one truth which could never be spoken. He did not return from his fifth attempt – we made up a story about his new life, involving sandy beaches and little gardens by the sea. Which was far more fun than the alternative.

Unsavoury characters dropped in from time to time: Sami, the mysterious man with long finger nails who slid documents under the door, and Rashid, our own, personal People Smuggler, with a mouth containing about three teeth, and a tattoo on his neck depicting an eagle shot through with an arrow.

My mother, having fallen pregnant soon after arrival in Jakarta, gave birth to her daughter only two months before we received our final call. And as we waded out to the waiting skiff, clutching our skinny life jackets, I thought about Omar who had always wanted to be a sailor, despite having no deeper experience of water than his bath tub.

The boat listed and slid, challenging each wave to a battle and losing every time. We rolled on the slippery deck, having failed to bag a spot up under the bows, where a group of young boys had dug in. When we weren't chilled by night spray, we were boiled by the sun. We pulled the giant tarp over our bodies the best we could, but water was already saturating the floor of the 30-foot boat carrying us to our new land. My new sister, Hadiya, looked like a pomegranate joined to a melon with bananas as arms and legs. A fruit child being eaten by monster waves and mosquitos. I smiled when I looked at her because she made me so sad.

My mother, starved of nutrition, barely recovered from the truck journey through Pakistan and life in a bare Jakarta flat for nearly a year, had then had to deal with a punishing childbirth. Exhausted on the floor of the boat, she prayed to Allah for mercy.

'He has forgotten us, Faisal', she said, staring out to an angry sea.

'He will remember again, you'll see', father replied, patting her wet hand.

Grandad was not there to offer a caustic comment, having refused to leave his *khawk*.

'There's no room in Australia for an old grunt like me', he said. 'Everything I am and have ever been is here. Everything that I ever will be.'

He had set off for a distant relative in Badakhshan, to take his chances on a new life; he liked the fact it was the only place in Afghanistan to resist the Taliban. I missed him dreadfully, as I missed Adeela, and Omar, and Cola. Poor Cola! One of our Kabul neighbours said he'd look after her but, when he had looked at the cat, his eyes were blank. Cola herself gave nothing away; she seemed accepting of her lot, I saw no questions in her round eyes. I remember how Adeela used to make her dance to Coldplay, her velvet paws outstretched – she took it in good heart; she was a mellow soul. I wondered how lonely my sister would be, abandoned to her city grave, with no-one left to tend her. She would have been excited by the boat trip, and the chance of a life where you didn't have to hide or pretend. But I think Adeela liked being a boy so much, she might have stuck with it. She saw how the world dealt with women, and despised it.

I don't know exactly when the boat ran into trouble. But I do know the sea was trying to claim us. First we lost our noodles, and then our blankets; then our bag of clothes slid over the side as the boat tipped and dipped, threatening to throw us into the water. I remember my beautiful sister Ghezaal drenched from head to toe, her hair hanging in wild strands over her face; my mother looked as if she might be losing her grip on Hadiya, her body spreadeagled across the deck by then, weighed down by the wet, heavy cloth of her robes. My father was shouting short, incomprehensible things, the baby was wailing as if the wretched, primal cries were being wrenched from her mouth by the wind which roared out of control, beside itself with fury.

God was indeed angry with us.

The boat went down.

The coldness of the water shocked me awake; until then, it felt as if the boat trip had been a dream. *There is only now*, grandad used to say. So this was now, and now seemed suspended, forever. Everything moved in slow motion – perhaps that was the effect of the water, whooshing and sloshing us around as if we were toys. That was the last time I saw Ghezaal, my mother and Hadiya, the little fruit. I fancied I heard Hadiya wailing for one last time; but everyone was screaming now, as they pleaded to God for a rescue which probably wouldn't come – it never had before – so all screams were equal.

That is what I dreamed. Ghezaal, mother and Hadiya submerged, their faces blurred through the wobbly water, arms no longer grasping, legs no longer kicking, voices no longer screeching, minds no longer frantic. Like Cola, they have accepted their lot. Further back, smaller and more distant, Adeela floats too – but her legs give little kicks because, like me, she was never good at swallowing the inevitable. She's cool too, though; it is a token gesture. Some things can't be resisted. It's not just the Taliban, then; even God, it seems, can't wait to dispose of the female of the species. In my life, the eradication is now complete.

Ghezaal had told me that Australia was the land of the blessed. Beaches wrapped the country in gold, fringed by oceans of turquoise velvet. This was a place where you could believe what you wanted to believe, wear what you wanted to wear, and work where you wanted to work, without fear or favour. Certainly without guns and stoning. With *Coldplay* playing in the background, of course. Cities stood tall and vibrant, ever ready to welcome you in.

In the event, my father and I were taken to a different country. My father said it was like being back in Kandahar. As we strained to see from the grubby windows of our bus, Curtin Detention Centre emerged from the desert like a mirage, a red Hell of baked-on dirt, massed fly attack and dejected bodies hanging around doing nothing. Our fellow survivors started murmuring, a fog of alarm seeping through the bus; a remaining baby cried suddenly, as if he had just remembered his mother was gone. One lady started wailing and rocking from side to side; an elderly man swore softly and violently in Dari. My father and I slipped into silence. Words had become irrelevant to us. Maybe our words had gone down with the ship and lay, even now, strewn about on the bottom of an uncaring sea. Maybe they were being used by Ghezaal, mother and Hadiya, who could no longer make their own.

I vaguely remembered being pulled from that numbing water by strong arms, feeling that all was lost; only later, on dry land, did I find my father again. It was only then we realised that our beloved women were gone for good.

Filing in through the razor wire which topped the centre's fences, I caught a glimpse of a skinny ginger cat mirroring my footsteps on the other side; a tiny trail of paw prints zig-zagged through the red soil, bending slightly as if the cat was drunk. My father was pulling me on, firmly, annoyed that I was hanging back, not realising that my world was spinning, and the deepest blue of the sky was getting mixed up with the red-brown of the soil, the cat smiling – sadly, hopefully, with quiet resignation – as I blacked out.

The cat, like the camp, was the other side of the Australian dream. The virus that killed me was part of nobody's dream; it was the ordinary nightmare of 'now' which my grandad understood so well. Perhaps I picked up this virus on the boat, or swallowed it in the rancid sea water. Whatever, I wanted to stay alive for the cat. It was the mountain cat of my grandad's story, impossible to kill. It was the cat who might re-attach me to this man, haul me back to the *khawk* of my earliest childhood, and wake up the dead – shake the life back into them – prop up the procession of lost souls I once called my family.

I was aware of my father grasping my hand; liquid like tears falling on my face; a burning in my head and behind my eyes as I waited for them to come. And at last! I sighted them. The camp gates were thrown open to release them . . . . . . Ghezaal willowy in her western clothes, Adeela strutting her boy-stuff, mother grumbling as she repositioned Hadiya on her hip, grandad plodding in with his wry grin, fresh-faced Omar carrying his red kite with pride, and Cola – yes, Cola! – padding in with cushioned feet, and long-suffering heart, and exquisitely knowing eyes which saw all things yet refused to panic, or despair, or long for redemption. I was beyond redemption then. Well, we all were. I thought for a moment that we might all be marching to freedom, but Cola shook her head. And that was that. It was cloud in my eyes; the product of a deluded, feverish mind.

There is no God but God.

There is no now but *now*.

There is no far celestial shore but, instead, this odd, misshapen reality which always has the capacity to turn out right, but so often doesn't.

Father wanted a proper Muslim funeral for me. I needed to be buried so my head faced towards Mecca, which was a nice idea. I think the gravedigger at the local town wanted to oblige – being a kind, if rather befuddled elderly man – but, in the event, I ended up facing towards the Derby Leprosarium, due to regulations ensuring all graves remained in their neat rows, without variation. At least I scored solid ground, unlike my mother and sisters, even now sloshing about in the deep blue sea, dissipating into shark bait.

My father, struggling with a deep depression now his family was gone, hated Derby, a baking and dusty little town strewn with drunken Aboriginal men and women seemingly beyond care. One man spoke to my father as he walked back to the van after my funeral; he expressed surprise that so many refugees were living just down the road. He pointed to the dirty, abandoned house he called home, and asked my father why he wanted to escape Afghanistan.

'Brudder, which end is up?' he said, his alcohol breath coming in rasps.

'We all refugees here. You just swapped one for the udder.'

I had to go home. I knew it and my father knew it. He had to rediscover his homeland *khawk*, and find his own father again. So the cycle could be complete.

But father was allowed to stay in his new country, giving him time to find accommodation, get a job and earn enough money to fly my broken little body back to Afghanistan. Just as well, then, that Afghans are such pragmatic people, ever willing to adapt to new situations and meet new demands.

He found my grandad, living on the tall slopes of Badakhshan, old and wizened now, but ever feisty. He had established dense orchards which gave him a comfortable living; he insisted on my father stepping in to the business so he could take a rest.

'Time for you to pull your finger out, my boy', he said, nodding sagely. 'Afghanistan is where the real work gets done.'

My father flew me home and buried me on the high pastures where nomads still roamed; in mountains so high that Marco Polo claimed even the birds couldn't fly there. Eventually my grandad, and then my father will lie beside me; we will sleep together beneath the deep snows of Winter, stilled in the silence of our icy tombs; fingered by the crystal cold of the Badakhshan air. Together we will feel the powerful fan of the eagle's wings as he soars overhead; we will sense the melting rivers of ice, and the scattered, brilliantly coloured wild flowers of Spring – the very Spring which was sold to pay for the Fighting Season. Perhaps my father will be able to buy it back, now, and start again.

I thought about the smiling cat of the story, who was lost to me. But as my father and grandfather turned to leave, and night dropped down swiftly, like a shroud, the paws of a snow leopard padded across the freshly turned soil of my grave, lightly kneading my spirit; letting me know that she was there, a seeker in the wilderness. A keeper of the *khawk*.

As I lost myself in the thick rug of her coat, I melted into the spots and circles which had already found their home.

ALISON WRAY

The Yellowstone Bear

Set back ten or eleven feet from the water's edge lay a huge red thing, the height of a table perhaps, but narrower, squarer, edge on. I had expected to see a bear, but I could not make this object be one. I ranged along the far bank of the stream, but saw nothing else. From a high tree a crow swooped towards the object and fluttered above it momentarily, before skirting away in an arc, back to its perch. Another bird, further away, gave a raucous cry but did not take flight.

I took my field glasses from their case, and put them to my eyes. The rubber immediately began to irritate my eczema. It took me a moment to find the place again, but then I saw the thing, and I saw what it was. The redness facing me was the raw flesh of a half-eaten animal, so large that it must be an elk. Dim through the thin mist over the water, a brown leg topped with a hoof hung above the grass. I tried to discern its angle, to know if the head or rump remained. The bird made another dive but would not land. So nervous. I started to search the grassland around the hulk, hoping for a sight of the bear. It must be somewhere close by. The crowd's hum barely troubled me.

'What is it, dad?' the boy whined. I didn't want to reply, so I stayed still. He was balancing on a small boulder to gain height, using his own glasses, the ones his mother gave him for the trip.

'Back half of an elk,' said someone. I half turned, and saw a ranger had come to the boy's far side. At his belt hung a can of bear spray, and he fingered its edge lightly as he spoke. I inspected the logo but didn't recognise it. I made a mental note to research what make of bear spray the rangers use.

'But where's the bear? Where's the bear?' the boy insisted. If his original question had been directed towards me, this one was not, for the bellyaching tone used with me was not there now. He sounded engaged, excited. Heat surged through my head and I gritted my teeth. Not here, not now.

The ranger pointed, and the boy traced the trajectory of his hand. I took up my glasses again, and followed the directions in his words.

'Down there to the left,' he said. 'Y'see where the big stone is in the stream, son? Just above that. He looks like an old tree stump, don't he?'

'Where, where?' the boy repeated, up on his toes. 'I don't see him.'

But I did. Now I did. The smallest hump of brown in the grass. I had missed it before. Stupid, stupid. You have to be smart, to see things like that, and I had not been smart enough. Janice says, 'Circumspection, Dan. Be circumspect'. I switched on circumspection and found a wry smile. So you screwed up, Dan, but no one knows, right? 'Cept you. Live with it, Dan. Enjoy the bear.

It was my first sight of a grizzly. Disappointingly underwhelming – something else to live with. My legs tightened and I made myself breathe out slowly. One, two, three. Then the boy twitched and I had to start all over again.

'Just you wait,' the ranger pacified the boy, 'in a while he'll move and then you'll see. You have to be patient in this game.'

Which game? The game of watching, of waiting? Of guarding, protecting, guiding? Over to my right, a man in a green tee-shirt placed a new long lens on his tripod camera. The game of photographing? Behind him several straggled rows of people whispered, pointed, and hopelessly fixed their phones on the scene. The game of being there, of having been there? How pathetic people were.

The breeze shifted and I caught a whiff of sulphur. All day I had breathed that hellish air and latterly hardly noticed its warm, toxic flavour. But out here, the light wind had been skirting the mountains in the north, and was fresher. So now I found a new pleasure in the infernal odour, and longed to be back by the geysers.

The boy was watching the dull, motionless shape of the bear. It would not take long till he lost interest, and then it would all begin again. His *I wants* and *can't we?*'s, time wasted looking for toilets, drinks, food he was prepared to eat, phone signals so he could call home. Relentless. But only three more days to go. Back to London. Drop him at his mother's. Out of there. 'Keep cool,' Janice said when our time was up. She walked me to her office door. 'Keep it cool.'

'I'm cold,' the boy said. I pulled his jacket from the back pack and threw it to him. He put it on without looking at me. As he did, the crowd around us stirred. I jolted my eyes back to the bear. It had raised its head momentarily and, as I found it in the grass, was just lowering it again. I only had time to catch a glimpse of ears and snout. Damn.

'What, what happened?' urged the boy to the ranger.

'Did ya miss it, son?' he replied. 'That's too bad. It goes so quick. But he'll do it again, you just watch.'

'What did he do?'

'For god's sake, it put its head up, that's all,' I told him. 'Nothing to get excited about.' The ranger turned towards me, but didn't speak.

'Nothing to get excited about,' the boy repeated with bravado.

Now the crowd was noisier, anticipating more action. Typical tourists. Traipsing out from their double-parked cars to look at the spectacle, like it was a fucking zoo. There ought to be some way to stop them at the gate, keep them out of it. Too many fucking people. 'Notice when the swearwords come,' Janice says. 'They're a clue.'

'What's the bear doing?' asked the boy.

'He's sleeping it off, son,' the ranger said. 'He just had that big meal, half an elk. So now he's sleepy.'

'Did he eat the whole half-an-elk himself?'

'That's a real smart question, son,' the ranger chuckled. I hated the patronising smile in his voice. 'I wasn't here right at the start, but some guy saw the kill this morning. He said there were two bears. This one – he's a last year's cub, or, no, probably the year before's, a two-year-old – and his mother.'

I shifted my glasses marginally to relieve the smarting of my skin, and started sweeping the grass for the mother. Nothing. I tried the woods beyond, but still I could not find it. If there was another bear, where was it? Stupid, stupid.

'Where's the mother bear gone?' the boy asked edgily. 'I don't see her.'

'Oh, she went off into the woods a while ago, before I got here,' the ranger said. The boy made a sort of whimpering sound.

'Is she ever coming back?' He did that kind of shudder thing he does. I clenched my fist.

'Coming back? Oh sure she is.' He put his hand on the boy's shoulder. I made to spring, but checked myself in time. Not here, not now.

'Hey, son,' the ranger went on soothingly. 'Did ya think she'd go off and leave the cub? She'd never do that. You know what, a mother never really leaves her cub.'

'Why?' the boy asked. He was so close he was fingering the ranger's badge.

'Well, for one thing, the big male bears are mighty dangerous. So a mother bear always keeps an eye on her cub, just in case there's a male about.'

'But not its daddy,' whispered the boy.

'Oh man,' smiled the ranger, 'sure, even its daddy. A cub's just not safe out on its own. That's why I'm certain the mother bear is here somewhere. Back there in the grass or just on the edge of the wood. You don't need to worry.'

The boy lowered his binoculars, and buried his hands deep in the pockets of his jacket.

But then the crowd roused again, and he quickly put the glasses back to his eyes.

'Look, look!' the boy cried. Everyone was looking.

The bear had raised its head and was staring over at the elk. Then its face turned in our direction, and it seemed to fix its gaze on me. Although I knew it could not see me, I stiffened, held my breath, and drank it in.

'Can he see us?' the boy asked apprehensively.

'Bears have really bad vision,' I said, not taking my eyes from my binoculars. The bear had raised its shoulders and was slowly lifting itself to its feet.

'Well…,' began the ranger, 'you're kinda right and kinda not right on that, sir.' I felt my chest tighten. The bear was fully standing now. The tee-shirt man clicked his swanky camera again and again. The crowd buzzed with excitement. In my peripheral vision a line of hands held out shiny flat oblongs and sent home blurred images of a dot.

'They see pretty well like we do, son.' It did not escape my notice that he was no longer addressing me. 'But it's true they are near-sighted.'

'So the bear can't see us?' the boy insisted.

'Hard to say, son, but I reckon he'd see us for sure if we made a lot of movement. So that's why we need to stay still.'

'Could he come and get us and eat us?'

'Obviously,' I told him. That boy should stop asking questions.

'You know what, son?' the ranger said soothingly, 'that's why I'm here, and all the other rangers.' I glanced towards him. He was caressing the spray again. 'Grizzlies are real dangerous. But you're safe here.'

The bear, mighty, glorious, took a bold, firm step. The crowd gasped and murmured. A renewed whiff of sulphurous air invaded my nostrils and I sucked it in. The bear turned its shoulders slowly this way and that. Then, its head raised, it looked again in my direction. Yes, look up here, on the hill above the stream. Here I am. I wondered if it could smell us. And then it started padding towards us, head low, swinging from left to right. I heard the ranger change his position, and the can was in his hand, cap off.

The boy made a moan, but continued to watch through his field glasses.

When the bear reached the water's edge, it stopped and lifted its head high, turning it, as if tasting the air. I bit my lip, willing it to plunge into the stream and cross to our side. It could be up the hill in moments.

But then it lowered its mouth to the water, and drank.

The crowd erupted into chatter. I tried to blank the noise out, find my space again. Our space, the bear's and mine. The skin around my eyes itched.

The boy made a kind of gurgling sound.

'Ya see?' the ranger said, 'There's no danger.'

The boy looked steadily through his glasses.

'Except what if he's drinking and …' His voice quavered, 'I wish… I wish I could see ...'

So, the bear would not come to me, then. But still it was a bear, my bear. Now, at the water, I had a proper view and was gratified. This was a creature to respect, and one that would respect me. If it did race up the hill, it would know me. Those fools would stand and click at the air until overwhelmed. It would fell one and make a meal of another. And it would look over at me, its brother, and be proud.

Strong, magnificent, the beast commanded the water's edge, the crows cowering beyond. I watched it lap at the water, its fur rippling as mighty muscles held its body in delicate balance on the sloping bank. My bear, colossus.

When it had done, it raised its head from the water and heaved itself backwards up to the meadow's edge. There it remained still for a moment, poised, head high, eyes fixed on the place where I stood. I stared back.

Then it turned around, its vast rump now towards me, first swaying slightly, then tensing. I held my breath. It would go to the elk and eat.

'What's he doing?' the boy asked. I focused on my prize.

The bear continued to stand. And then, quite suddenly, shifted its hind legs, tensed and pissed into the grass.

The crows rose yelling into the air. The onlookers shifted and babbled. The ranger sniggered. The boy giggled. I spun around. Faintly, from the dark woods, I heard Janice call my name.

But I could not see her.

FLASH FICTION FIRST PRIZE

KIT DE WAAL

Crushing Big

The Mother has four children and is never late. She wears her cagoule like a fur coat. I wonder if I'm in love.

She brings cinnamon cakes for the school fair still warm from her Aga. She smiles at me because she smiles at everyone and offers me a bun on the sly. She winks and I wonder if I'm in love.

Our children walk home together after sports day and she links my arm. Her angora cardigan catches on my watch and we put our heads together to untangle. I would rather not. I would be chained to her forever.

My daughter is 'crushing big' on her son. She wants to be his girlfriend she says and I am jealous of her guileless desire, her expectation of a happy ending. I tell the Mother and she laughs. I can see down her clean throat, glimpse her beating heart. I could jump in. I could drown.

At my birthday party I take her coat, lay it neatly under my mattress and wait for the guests to go. 'Did I bring a jacket' she asks swaying at the front door. I do a dance of uncertainty, check the cupboard, swear I'm too drunk to remember.

I do not sleep. I am in love. I feel her shape beneath me. She will have fluff in her pocket, a bus ticket, a baby's button. And tomorrow, when the children are at school, I will wrap her arms around me, hold her close.

FLASH FICTION SECOND PRIZE

AILEEN BALLANTYNE

The Witness

I remember the terracotta pots that held the geraniums, and the smell of new paint on the windows and walls when they cut off her hair that day. The girls and the women smelled the paint-smell and it calmed them. Naked and quiet, they laid clothes and shoes by the pots that held the geraniums.

When it was done the Ukrainians took long wooden poles, each with a curved metal hook, pulled each body in by piercing its mouth. The dentists came then to tear out gold teeth. I considered some time before watching at Belzec that day to write up my hygiene report. I could not conclude, on that day at least, that bodies were disposed of in a sanitary way.

The voices run on a loop: an old woman with numbers on her arm, talking of ripples and pools, circles subsiding, memory a stone in its depth now. I could not see clearly that day: steam misted the porthole. I look through the glass now at the things we left behind: the glass from the cold beer we drank, a pot for cooking, a bow for a dress, grey buttons and spoons, and a red Bakelite thimble like the one on the finger of the fair-haired girl. Broken now, cracked by a stone or a foot; splayed like the petals of a geranium.

FLASH FICTION THIRD PRIZE

SANDY TOZER

Sense of Smell

It starts with the scent of water. People will tell you it doesn't smell – at least when you are in it, swimming in it, diving through it, burrowing in the bath maybe; even, or especially, when you are submerged in it all the time. In the womb stretching through the waters, can you smell the ambergris and corn on the morning after your mother, your universal being, has woken from a strange dream? After she's slept with her man, and held the cat, held her close, nose in the fur – damp citrus from the rain and grass outside. After she's eaten cornbread, buttered, and drunk illicit coffee. Do you, as you turn in your bounded sea, think that it is a good day, a new day to spin over in your ocean? As you push down, the turning earth flies forward in ellipses around the sun, also flying, all things moving through the cool of space.

They will say space doesn't smell.

The baby knows different.

And after the swim at the busy pool, the chlorine stripping the walls, the spills of drink outside; there is a whiff of charnel cigarette, the chemical fires of a couple of schoolkids leaning against the wall, watching the pregnant woman pass. A scant brush with the deathly, the taint that wakes the baby inside who wrinkles her nose.

Let's begin.

DORSET PRIZE

MARIA DONOVAN

Chess

Before he went to school, before he even had breakfast, Michael sent his dad a message: 'Pawn to Queen's Knight 4'.

'Who are you texting?' said Nan. She didn't sit with him at the table: she was getting his lunch ready, checking his school bag. Michael didn't answer. She said, 'I'm running late,' and took the radio upstairs. He chewed his toast and the sound was loud inside his head, like giant ants marching across a desert of sugar. He saw time passing on his phone.

His father had until seven o'clock that evening to answer or lose the game.

At school he had the phone on silent but Mrs Bradbury said, 'Michael?' At the end of the day she gave him back his phone and looked as if she might say something then closed her mouth again.

They all kept saying it wasn't Michael's fault.

After tea, he sat in his room. He looked at the chessboard and his brain felt like a slug trying to cross a motorway. The radio downstairs sent out gusts of laughter.

Michael stared at his phone: 6.59. He tried to stop the numbers changing. He closed his eyes and put his hands over his ears but still heard the pips for the seven o'clock news and the theme tune for 'The Archers'.

Michael toppled the white king. He set him on his feet again. Turning the chess board round, he tried to be his dad working out the next move.

FRANNY FRENCH

Encounter

God was following me on I-5. I cruised to the shoulder – the ultimate pullover. This is it, I thought – death. OK … well, that would solve my money problems.

I walked over to the vehicle. God was not what I'd expected. First off, was God a he or a she? Also, God was a midget.

God stared straight ahead, sighing in a mildly put-out way.

'Did I … do something wrong?' I asked.

'Just get in,' God said.

So I did.

'How do you reach the pedals?' I said.

God's legs lengthened. Before we'd gone a mile, God was an aging, bearded African-American guy. Then God was a plus-size white lady in a purple running suit. Then a very tall East Indian teenage boy, ducking his head to fit beneath the roof. Then a sleek Italian woman with super long nails.

'Do you think you could stop doing that?'

Nodding, God settled on a middle-aged American Indian woman with a perm and a 'Not My Problem' T-shirt.

'Where we going?' I said.

'Anywhere you want,' God said, kind of puffing up.

'Well, I'm sort of hungry. I didn't know I'd be doing this today.'

'What's your favorite food?'

'Depends,' I said. 'Are you paying?'

God drove without answering. He was now a little white girl in pink, driving all pissed-off looking.

I searched my brain for some question to ask, but came up blank. Worried about my finances again, I was no closer to God than I'd ever been.

SARAH TAYLOR

Good at Crisps

We got good at crisps as we grazed our ways through packet after packet on rainy afternoons in pub car parks, on days when there was no home game. Walkers Roast Chicken, KP Cheese and Onion, billowing pillows of Golden Wonder Smokey Bacon, we tasted them all. Trying them every which way, crunching them, sucking them, licking them, squashing the packet and pouring crisp crumbs down our throats 'til we choked. Fitting big ones in sideways and stretching our mouths so the salt got in the cracks at the corners where a smile used to come. In distant pub gardens, we discovered exotic flavours, our tongues teased with Worcester Sauce and Prawn Cocktail. And we learnt to suck on crinkle-cut Seabrooks, making them last, playing crisp games to pass the time. Who could eat the whole packet without licking their lips? Who could keep one on their stuck-out tongue the longest? Thinking we could change destiny if we were good and nice as we watched from steamed-up windscreens as they brought over the tray, her with pinch-faced pride and him with guilty wallet. On days less wet, we tried to play like real children on rusting customer facilities left there for kids like us. And then, sharp partings and us hugged to near death. His breath all man and with his bitter-top moustache.

SHERRI TURNER

The Price of Truth

The man on the Tube was not a beggar. I knew this because it said so on the cards he placed on the seats next to each passenger. He wanted a job.

'I'll give you a job,' I said. 'A short one. Sit with me till the end of the line and tell me something interesting about your life and I'll give you twenty quid.'

'Why?' he asked.

Because I had run out of ideas? Because my own life was too ordinary? Because I was too lazy to make something up?

'Do you want the money or not?'

He did.

'What do you want to know?'

'You choose. But make it real and make it something I haven't heard before.'

So he talked.

He told me of his family: drunken father, slattern mother, a struggle of a childhood.

'Heard it,' I said. 'Not good enough.'

He told me about a job he'd had, a marriage and a child, and losing them all.

'Heard it.'

He told me about the streets, the drugs, the doorways.

'Old news. Tell me your truth.'

So he told me about a man he once met, a man who had heard it all and never listened, a man who thought the only worthwhile stories were new stories, a man who thought you could buy a life you hadn't lived for twenty quid and then just get off the train.

I hadn't heard that before, so I gave him the money.

Biographies

David Gaffney lives in Manchester. He is the author of several books including *Sawn-Off Tales* (2006), *Aromabingo* (2007), *Never Never* (2008), *The Half-Life of Songs* (2010) and *More Sawn-Off tales* (2013). He has written articles for *The Guardian*, *Sunday Times*, *Financial Times* and *Prospect* magazine. 'One hundred and fifty words by Gaffney are more worthwhile than novels by a good many others.' *The Guardian*. www.davidgaffney.org

Roger McGough is one of Britain's best-loved and prolific poets. He first came to prominence in 1967 when his work was included in the Penguin anthology *The Mersey Sound: Penguin Modern Poets 10* which has since sold over a million copies. Much travelled and translated, his poetry gained increasing popularity, especially from its widespread use in schools. He is twice winner of the Signal Award for best children's poetry book and recipient of the Cholmondeley Award.

In 1997 Roger was awarded an O.B.E. for his services to poetry and he is a Fellow of the Royal Society of Literature, Honorary Fellow of Liverpool John Moores University and an Honorary Professor at Thames Valley University. He has an MA from the University of Northampton and D. Litts from the universities of Hull, Liverpool, Roehampton and The Open University. He was recently honoured with the Freedom of the City of Liverpool. Roger presents *Poetry Please* on BBC Radio 4 – the longest running poetry programme broadcast anywhere in the world. His latest book *It Never Rains* is the 100th to be published.

Jane Rogers has written eight novels including *Mr Wroe's Virgins* (which she dramatised as an award-winning BBC drama serial), *Her Living Image* (Somerset Maugham Award), *Island,* and *Promised Lands* (Writers Guild Best Fiction Award). Her most recent novel *The Testament of Jessie Lamb* was longlisted for the 2011 ManBooker prize, and won the Arthur C Clarke Award 2012. Her short story collection, *Hitting Trees with Sticks* was shortlisted for the 2013 Edgehill Award. She also writes radio drama and adaptations. Jane is Professor of Writing at Sheffield Hallam University and is a Fellow of the Royal Society of Literature. www.janerogers.org

Cait Atherton (born on the Isle of Man) worked for many years for the NHS in Cambridge and London as an audiological scientist. Moving to SE Asia with her family however enabled her to scratch the long-felt itch to write. In recent years her stories have found success achieving a win with Meridian Writing (2012); long list for the Fish Prize (2011); short list for the Fish Prize (2012) and a Highly Commended in the Bristol Prize (2012). Her story 'The Homecoming' appears in *A Tail for All Seasons vol IV* published by Priory Press Ltd. (2015). She was selected for mentorship by Cinnamon Press and is working on her first novel. She helped organise the first English language Literary Festival in Bangkok, edits SALA Magazine for the National Museum Volunteers Bangkok and also creates websites for charity. More about Cait can be found at: www.watercolourwords.com

Aileen Ballantyne is a former national newspaper journalist turned poet, based in Edinburgh. She was the staff medical correspondent for the *Guardian*, then *The Sunday Times*. She now works as a tutor in English and Scottish Literature at the University of Edinburgh where she recently completed a PhD in Creative Writing and Modern Poetry. She was a Reuters Journalism Fellow studying medical ethics at Green College, Oxford, and her investigative journalism for the *Guardian* has twice been commended in the British Press Awards. Aileen won the University of Edinburgh Sloan prize for poetry (2009) and the National Galleries of Scotland poetry prize (2011); she was commended in the Edwin Morgan international poetry prize, (2011) is a past winner of the Wigtown Book Festival poetry competition (2012). In 2015 Aileen won first prize in the Mslexia Poetry Competition, the short poem category at the Poetry on the Lake competition at Orta St Giulia and was commended in the Hippocrates Prize for Poetry and Medicine. 'The Witness' was her first attempt at flash fiction – but won't be her last – she is currently working on both poetry and prose and on the 'final editing and honing' of her first collection of poetry.

Matt Barnard is a poet and short story writer. His poems have been published in a number of magazines, including *Acumen, London Magazine, Magma, Other Poetry* and *Outposts*. He featured in the Poetry School's 2004 anthology *Entering the Tapestry* and in 2006 won The Poetry Society's Hamish Canham Prize with his poem 'The Sore Thumb'. In 2015, he won the Ink Tears national short story competition with 'The

Last Damn Peach'. He is married with two children and two dogs. www.mattbarnardwriter.com

Lisa Blower is an award-winning short story writer and novelist with a PhD in Creative & Critical Writing (Bangor University, 2011) where she taught on their creative writing programme for 5 years. She won *The Guardian*'s National Short Story competition in 2009 and was shortlisted for the BBC National Short Story Award in 2013. Her work has appeared in *The Guardian, Comma Press, The New Welsh Review, The Luminary, Short Story Sunday* and on Radio 4. Her debut novel *Sitting Ducks* is out spring, 2016. She is currently working on her first short story collection *It's Gone Dark over Bill's Mother's*. She regularly hosts creative writing workshops on short fiction and continues to pursue her academic research into the role of gender and identity in online self-narratives. She lives in Shrewsbury.

Nicolas Burbidge has laboured in the some of the deeper, canary-killing mines of the media, public and charity sectors for 20 years. In 2014, he completed with distinction an MA in Creative & Life Writing at Goldsmiths, University of London where his portfolio was shortlisted for the Pat Kavanagh Award. Nick writes short stories and poetry and has recently begun the messy business of writing a novel. He also writes articles for culture and fashion magazine *She Ra*, which you can find at www.sheramag.com/author/nick-burbidge/.

Sarah Burton teaches Creative Writing at the University of Cambridge. Her publications include: *Impostors: Six Kinds of Liar* (Viking, 2000); *A Double Life: a Biography of Charles and Mary Lamb* (Viking, 2003); *The Miracle in Bethlehem: A Storyteller's Tale* (Floris, 2008); *How to Put on a Community Play* (Aurora Metro, 2011); *The Complete and Utter History of the World by Samuel Stewart, Aged 9 (*Short Books, 2013). Her next book, *H*, is a novel.

Melanie Cheng is a writer, mum and general practitioner based in Melbourne, Australia. Her writing has appeared in many Australian literary journals including the *Griffith Review*, *Overland* and *Sleepers Almanac*. She is currently working on a short story collection. melaniechengwriter.wordpress.com

Tom Collingridge read Philosophy at Hull, worked as a teacher in Zimbabwe and England, at various local authorities, and for Sport England helping set up the World Class athlete programme. He moved to the Netherlands in 2003, where he works as a freelance copywriter and translator. He was also the driving force behind the creation of the Dutch National Poetry Competition, now a major event in the country's literary calendar. Over the years Tom has won a few minor prizes in smaller poetry and short story competitions, and had the occasional poem published. This poem was the first work he had submitted to anyone in nearly a decade. www.tomcollingridge.com

Julia Deakin was born in Nuneaton and worked her way north via the Potteries, Manchester and York to Huddersfield, where she began writing poems on a poetry MA. Her three acclaimed collections are *The Half-Mile-High Club* (a 2007 Poetry Business Competition winner), *Without a Dog* (Graft Poetry, 2008) and *Eleven Wonders* (Graft Poetry, 2012). Widely published, she has won numerous prizes and featured twice on *Poetry Please*. 'Reading is a perk of the job,' she says. 'If only it were a job.' More details at www.juliadeakin.co.uk

Maria Donovan is from Bridport and went to school at the Visitation Convent, St Catherine's Primary and Colfox. She trained as a nurse while living in Holland and speaks fluent Dutch. In another life as a musician and performer she travelled Europe and later switched careers to become Senior Lecturer in Creative Writing at the University of Glamorgan. Maria has published a collection of flash fiction, *Tea for Mr Dead*, and a collection of short stories, *Pumping Up Napoleon*. 'Chess' is a spin-off from her unpublished novel, *The Chicken Soup Murder*, which is a finalist in this year's Dundee International Book Prize. Maria now lives in Bridport.

Michael Derrick Hudson lives in Fort Wayne, Indiana, USA where he works for the Allen County Public Library. His poems have appeared in *Poetry, Boulevard, Georgia Review*, *Gulf Coast*, *River Styx*, *New Ohio Review*, and other journals. He was co-winner of the 2014 Manchester Poetry Prize.

Kit de Waal is published in various anthologies (*Fish Prize 2011 & 2012*; *The Sea in Birmingham 2013*; *Final Chapters 2013* and *A Midlands*

Odyssey 2015) and on Radio 4 Readings. She came second in the Costa Short Story Prize 2014 with 'The Old Man & The Suit', second in the Bath Short Story Prize 2014 with 'The Beautiful Thing' and second in the Bare Fiction Flash Fiction Prize. She won the Readers' Prize at the Leeds Literary Prize 2014, and the Bridport Prize for Flash Fiction 2014. Her first novel *My Name is Leon* will be published by Penguin in June 2016.

Judith Edelman is a native New Yorker, who now splits her time between La Jolla, CA, Nashville, TN, and – periodically – a Maine island twelve miles out to sea. The daughter of a Nobel Prize-winning scientist and a kindergarten teacher, she has been nominated twice for the Pushcart Prize and was the recipient of *The Pinch Journal*'s 2011 Literary Prize in fiction, as well as a finalist for the Calvino Prize and the Tennessee Williams Fiction Prize. Her stories have appeared in the *Gettysburg Review*, the *Bellevue Literary Review* and *Hayden's Ferry Review*, among other journals. She received her MFA in fiction from the Bennington College Writing Seminars in 2011. In her years as a touring singer-songwriter, she recorded four albums in Nashville on the Compass Records and Thirty Tigers labels, as well as touring extensively in the U.S. and U.K. She has also composed music for documentaries showing on PBS' Nova, Channel Four London, and at the Sundance Film Festival, among other venues. www.judithedelman.com

Ken Evans completed his Master's in Creative Writing at the University of Manchester in 2015. He works part-time as a lead-mine guide at the Heights of Abraham to what is laughably called help 'support', his poetry habit. When not underground, he teaches Creative Writing classes for the WEA.

Mark Fiddes lives in South London and works in Soho. His first poetry pamphlet *The Chelsea Flower Show Massacre* (Templar Poetry) was published in March. Shortlisted in the 2015 Saboteur Award, it also featured as poetry book of the month by Lovereading.com. Awards and commendations include the Gregory O'Donoghue, Philip Larkin, Charles Causley, Live Canon, Wasafiri and Frogmore Prizes. https://markfiddes.wordpress.com/

Franny French lives in Portland, Oregon, USA. Her fiction and poetry have appeared in national and international literary journals and anthologies, including *The Ledge Poetry & Fiction Magazine*, *Enizagam* and *St. Petersburg Review*. She is the recipient of Portland State University's Burnham Award for Fiction and an Oregon Literary Fellowship.

Ian Harker lives in Leeds. His work has appeared in *Agenda*, *Other Poetry*, *The North*, and *Stand*. He was shortlisted for the Bridport prize in 2014, as well as for the Troubadour and Guernsey International competitions. Shortlisted for Templar Poetry's Straid and Portfolio awards, he was chosen as one of the 2015 Pamphlet Award winners, and his debut, 'The End of the Sky', is forthcoming from Templar later in 2015.

Joanna M Herrmann lives and works in the Welsh Borders. Her professional background is in mental health, where she hears many remarkable stories of ordinary lives. This has led her to have an interest in narrative as a basic human need. She also has an interest in short fiction, and in developing the creative boundary of non-fiction. She is working on a collection of short stories, and 'Ice Injuries: Halvmaneoya Island, Winter 1970' is the first of these to be published.

John Hobart is a freelance editor and proofreader. He lives in Newcastle upon Tyne. You can find his essay 'The Song I Could Not Stop Singing' at the literary website The Millions.

William Konarzewski was born in Bexhill-on-sea, Sussex. His father was Polish. He was educated at Winchester College and studied medicine at Guy's Hospital. Currently he works as a consultant anaesthetist in Colchester. Outside medicine, his main interest is writing and he has self-published three novels since 2014. He is married with two children.

Liz Lefroy won the 2011 Roy Fisher Prize resulting in the publication of her first pamphlet, *Pretending the Weather.* Her sequence, *The Gathering,* was set to music by Brian Evans and first performed at the St Chad's Music Festival, Shrewsbury, in 2012. *Mending the Ordinary* (2014) is published by Fair Acre Press. Liz's work has appeared in *Mslexia; The Frogmore Papers; Magma; Shoestring; Ink, Sweat and Tears; Wenlock Poetry Festival anthologies 2013 and 2015; The Emergency Poet Anthology* and on the *Writers' Hub*. She reads regularly at poetry festivals and literary events, including performances at the

Edinburgh Fringe of her dramatic sequence, *The Seven Rages of Woman*. She hosts the Poetry Busk at Wenlock Poetry Festival, is organiser of Shrewsbury Poetry and presents 'Poetry Round-up' on Ryan Kennedy's show on BBC Radio Shropshire. Liz is a senior lecturer in Social Work at Glyndwr University in Wrexham. http://lizlefroy.wix.com/liz-lefroy Blog: http://someonesmumsays.blogspot.co.uk/

Annie MacConnel is a graduate of the MFA Program For Writers at Warren Wilson College. She is a freelance editor in Minneapolis, Minnesota, where she lives with her husband and son. This is her first published story.

Kathy Miles is a poet and short story writer. Born in Liverpool, she moved to Wales in 1972 and lives near Aberaeron. A trained librarian, she is currently studying for an MA in Creative Writing at the University of Wales, Trinity Saint David. Her first collection, *The Rocking Stone*, was published by Poetry Wales Press, and *The Shadow House* by Cinnamon Press in 2009. Her third collection of poems, *Gardening With Deer*, is due to be published by Cinnamon Press in June 2016. Her work has appeared in many anthologies and magazines, and she has also been highly placed in several competitions, including first place in the 2014 Welsh Poetry Competition and the 2013 Second Light Short Poem Competition. Kathy Miles is a founder-member of the Lampeter Writers' Group, run by Gillian Clarke, and a member of Wales PEN Cymru and The Welsh Academy. She reads with the Red Heron performance group, and has read at many festivals and local events. http://www.poetrypf.co.uk/kathymilesbiog.shtml

Helen Morris lives and works in Essex and started writing short stories in 2014. Her stories have been published in *Solstice Shorts* by Arachne Press, *Goose* published by the University of Toronto, *Crooked Holster* published by Crooked Holster, *And Fresher Writing 2015* published by Bournemouth University and in the *Bedford Writing Competition: Short Story Anthology 2014*. She is on Twitter @mortaltaste if anyone wants to say 'hello'.

Helen Paris is co-artistic director of Curious theatre company. Solo performances include *Family Hold Back*, which toured in the UK and internationally, including Sydney Opera House, Guling Street Avant-Garde Theater, Taipei and the Center for the Contemporary Arts, Shanghai.

Curious has produced over 40 projects in performance and film. The work has been presented and supported by institutions including the Royal Shakespeare Company, British Council Showcase at the Edinburgh Festival and film festivals including the London Short Film Festival and Hors Pistes at the Pompidou Center. Curious is produced by Artsadmin. Paris is a professor of performance at Stanford University, USA.

Wendy Riley was brought up in the English town of Hereford and now lives in Melbourne, Australia, with her husband and son. A journalist, she loves writing of all kinds, but creative writing is her passion, with two novel manuscripts now finalised. 'Amir's Story' belongs in a completed compilation of 12 short stories, *A Book of Broken Pieces*, currently seeking a publisher.

C.E.J. Simons is a British-Canadian poet born in Winnipeg, Canada. He is a Senior Associate Professor of British Literature in Tokyo. His previous jobs have included professional martial artist, rodent euthanizer, and M.P. staffer. In 2003 he held the Harper-Wood Studentship in Creative Writing at St John's College Cambridge. He has published on Wordsworth, Shakespeare, Yeats, Emily Dickinson, and Sylvia Plath, most recently contributing a chapter to the *Oxford Handbook of William Wordsworth* (Oxford University Press, 2015). Two of his previous pamphlets were nominated for the CBC (Canadian Broadcasting Corporation) Canada Writes poetry prize. His poems have won prizes in UK competitions including the Cardiff International Poetry Competition and the Wigtown Competition. His criticism and poetry have appeared in publications including the *Independent*, *Isis*, *Magma, Oxford Poetry*, *PN Review*, and *The Times Literary Supplement*.

James Stradner graduated from Goldsmiths in 2014 with a BA in Fine Art and Art History. His poetry has been featured in *ANTHOLOGY I* and *II* (2014 and 2015) published by AOTCS Press. In March 2015 he curated s*mall birds nest with blue eggs inside* at MMX Gallery in London and was an Associate Artist at Firstsite, Colchester for 2015-16. www.jamesstradner.co.uk

Sarah Taylor recently completed an MA in English at Oxford Brookes University. Although she lives in the south of England with her three children, Sarah's roots - and much of the inspiration for her writing - are back in her native Nottingham. She was Highly Commended in the Flash

Fiction category of the Bridport Prize in 2012. Writing Flash Fiction fits in well with mum-stuff and Sarah's three part-time jobs but her biggest goal in the coming year has to be to finish her first novel!

Sandy Ann Tozer writes fiction and poetry and is currently working on a graphic novel. She has published a few poems and a story in anthologies. A founder member of a writing group of four writers and artists she also has an MA in Creative Writing & Authorship from the University of Sussex. Sandy is new to flash fiction and lives near Brighton in the UK.

Sherri Turner was brought up in Cornwall and now lives in Surrey with her husband. She has had numerous short stories published in women's magazines in the UK and abroad and has won prizes for both poetry and short stories in competitions including the Bristol Prize, the New Writer prize, the Writer's Bureau Short Story competition and the Grace Dieu poetry competition. In 2015 she was the joint winner of the inaugural Plough Short Story competition. Her work has also appeared in a number of short story anthologies and her first short story collection is currently under consideration.

Eoghan Walls lectures in Creative Writing at Lancaster University. He has received an Eric Gregory Award, an Irish Arts Council Bursary and his first collection, The Salt Harvest, was published by Seren in 2011. It was short listed for the Strong Award for Best First Collection.

Alison Wray grew up in north-west London. She gained a first class degree and a doctorate in linguistics from the University of York, and during her early thirties developed dual career as a linguistics lecturer and professional classical singer. She currently works at Cardiff University, where she is a professor of language and communication. She has published numerous academic papers and several research and textbooks, including *Formulaic language: pushing the boundaries* (Oxford University Press, 2008) and *Formulaic language and the Lexicon* (Cambridge University Press, 2002) which won the 2003 book prize of the British Association for Applied Linguistics. *Projects in Linguistics* (Hodder, 1998) was shortlisted in 1999 for the same prize, and is now in its third edition. Another successful textbook, *Critical Reading and Writing for Postgraduates* (Sage) will appear in its third edition in 2016. Alison's current research writing concerns the patterns of communication between people with dementia and their carers.

What people say about the Bridport Prize

Winning the Bridport Prize was an overwhelming and wonderful experience. Sometimes we can isolate ourselves as writers. The Bridport Prize introduced me to a fascinating group of people from around the world who love art and who struggle in different ways with writing, which was comforting and inspiring beyond belief. I would encourage anyone who is nervous about submitting their work to have a little faith and go for it.
Natalya Anderson, (Canada) 1st Prize, Poetry 2014

Coming second in the 2014 Bridport Prize short story competition gave me a huge boost in confidence in my writing. So much so that it spurred me on to quit my job, finish my novel and get it off my laptop and out into the world.
Sean Lusk, (UK) 2nd Prize, Short Story, 2014

I was so honored to be recognized by the Bridport Prize this year. It's an award series that is well recognized, not just for the generous prizes, but also because of its prestigious reputation. Thank you to the Bridport Arts Centre for supporting writers and for creating a wonderful and welcoming community of writers!
Tori Sharpe, (USA) 2nd Prize, Poetry, 2014

Receiving a Highly Commended in the Bridport Prize Competition has been such an encouragement for me to keep writing. It's more than the prize itself; it's the validation that comes from people acknowledging the power of your work.
Katherine Swinson, (USA), Highly Commended, Poetry, 2014

The Bridport Prize is one of the most prestigious awards for emerging writers today, and to be recognized as a prizewinner is an incredible honor. Since then, my stories have gone on to be prizewinners in the Alice Munro Short Story Competition.
William Pei Shih (USA) Highly Commended, Short Story, 2014

Coming 3rd in the Bridport Prize for Flash Fiction was a wonderful surprise for me. To see my own work in the anthology alongside writing of such a high standard was a real confidence boost.
Michael Conley, 3rd Prize, Flash Fiction, 2014

I shortlisted for the Bridport Prize in 2012, and the very story that shortlisted – 'How to be Brave' – is one I then, as a result, felt confident enough to develop into a novel. I'm so excited that I eventually got a book deal and that the novel was published in September 2015. I always tell people I shortlisted for your great prize (actually twice!) as it is one of my great achievements.
Louise Beech, Highly Commended, Short Story, 2012